John 'Bad John, Devil John' is a
descendant of our Solomon H. Wright Sr.
Born in Pennsylvania

Phillip K. Epling, author

Bad John Wright

THE LAW

of

PINE
MOUNTAIN

By: Phillip K. Epling

The Overmountain Press

JOHNSON CITY, TENNESSEE

ISBN 1-57072-073-8
Copyright © 1981 by Phillip K. Epling
Reprinted 1997 by The Overmountain Press
Printed in the United States of America

1 2 3 4 5 6 7 8 9 0

Contents

Introduction

Bad John Wright was a name well known in the hills of Pine Mountain, not as an outlaw, but as a heroic protector of the law and the people he loved, who chose the atmosphere of the quiet and rugged mountains to settle and live a moral and peaceful life.

Their only hope was that it would never change, but some men do change, and some become oppressors of the innocent. Bad John felt responsible in seeing that this did not happen.

He was not named *"Bad"* John Wright by the innocent, but by those whose crude desire it was to conquer and overpower, and to seize by force whatever could be impetuously taken with the flash of a gun. John Wright knew only one law—the law of Pine Mountain—which he considered the knowledge given him from birth: "To know what was right and what was wrong."

John was not a lawyer. He didn't have to be, he thought. He knew it was wrong for anyone to forcefully overpower the innocent—the weaker individual—and feast upon what they could greedily seize illegally. To John there could be only one loser, and he felt the lawman had to win to protect the mountain peaceful way of life. Therefore, the outlaw had to lose, one way or the other!

Much time and effort were devoted to this research in gathering the true historical facts as herein related, for which the author extends thanks and much credit to G.

C. Ratliff (deceased) and his son, Paul E. Ratliff, for their research and devotion in gathering these historical facts. Ninety-five percent was given voluntarily by John Wright himself, and the other 5 percent from Martha Jane Wright (both now deceased).

The name Bad John Wright has been long and frequently discussed without regard to justice and his moral character. Mainly his original aim was to bring the outlaws into custody without bodily harm to either side if possible. In doing this he many times succeeded, but he too sometimes regretfully failed, which resulted in fierce gunfights and bloodshed.

Was there a better way? Could the laws of Pine Mountain have been more peacefully or securely enforced otherwise? May we ask: "Could the old West have been won differently by the early settlers?" You be the judge as we read *Bad John Wright—The Law of Pine Mountain.*

Phillip K. Epling

"Bad" John Wright was one of the settlers who lived in the Jenkins area at the turn of the century when coal companies were opening up southeastern Kentucky for coal mining. As a U.S. deputy marshal he enforced the law with a firm hand. The name "Bad" or "Devil" given to him was meant to be complimentary by law abiding citizens . . . that he was bad for the lawbreakers. "The Trail of the Lonesome Pine" is based on happenings in the life of John Wright in character, "Devil Jud Tolliver."

John Wright at about age fifty from an
old tintype picture.

Just over the mountain from Jenkins a few miles away, we see here a chain driven motor truck on the way to Hellier in Pike County, September 16, 1911. Through rough mountain terrain, roads were built by men, working voluntarily each man six days per year, without pay from anybody.

George W. Kinney of Pike County, Kentucky. Kinney helped chase Indians after the Custer Massacre and saw Sitting Bull killed. He and John Wright were friends.

Chapter I

Background of the Mountain Feudists

Passion, revenge, murder: these are not words unique to the mountain sections of Kentucky and neighboring states. But in the Southern Appalachians during the years of the various feuds, these somber words of death took to themselves an intensity unparalleled in American history. To understand the vindictiveness of the mountain feudists it is necessary to know something of the background and the character of these people.

During the years from 1750 to 1770 the early pioneers —Dr. Thomas Walker, James McBride, John Finley, Christopher Gist, Daniel Boone, and others—made hunting and exploring expeditions into the wilderness with the founding of homes uppermost in their minds. Invariably, when these men returned to their settlements in the fertile Shenandoah and other valleys, they gave vivid reports of the bounteous new land they had found.

At this time there were two great human tides flowing toward Cumberland Gap: one, which had crossed the Blue Ridge Mountains, was pressing up the Shenandoah

1

Valley, the other coming up the Savannah River Valley, ever pushing the frontier westward.

These liberty loving people had landed upon savage shores of the hitherto unknown American continent. Hostile Indians were their skeptical hosts. They had undergone hunger and disease. Now, they combined to form the two flowing tides of humans bound slowly but surely for Cumberland Gap.

The weaklings, the tenderfeet, and the faint-hearted had perished on the way or had returned to Europe to submit again to tyranny, save for those who, desiring neither to re-cross the ocean nor to brave the threatening wilderness, settled in the towns of the coast.

The sturdy people who chose to advance upon the wilderness were very unlike their brethren who had settled upon the shores of New England. The former were from the rural districts of England, Ireland, etc., while the New Englanders came principally from the densely populated districts of England. City bred, these people did not care for the hardships of border life. Therefore they founded towns and developed industries. On the other hand their brethren from the rural areas were unacquainted with the industrial arts and cared nothing for them, preferring to live in the great open spaces, own land if possible, and be free to think and act for themselves.

And so the sturdy ones formed into the two tides of human expansion westward, until at last the two met in the Holston and Clinch River region in western North Carolina and Virginia. Here they heard of the fabled Kentucky region and, hearing, they set out to see for themselves. They traveled in small bands, and drove their sheep, cattle, and hogs before them. They walked with cautious step, for they were in constant danger of attack from crafty Indians, who crouched in the thick rhododendron or behind the omnipresent trees.

2

Once across the rugged Cumberland, these first Kentuckians were separated from the eastern settlements by an almost impassable mountain, Pine Mountain, shut in by deep and gloomy forests, and haunted on all sides by hostile savages. And so there men worked and fought, and tried to mold the new country after their own ideals. But, while they worked and fought, their environment molded *them* into rude backwoodsmen.

The War Between the States forced unwanted decisions upon the mountain people. As a matter of preference the majority of the mountaineers would have held themselves aloof from the conflict, letting the slaveholders of the South fight the battle with the antislavery North, *had there been no other issue than slavery.*

The hill people cared nothing for the Negro in any sense, except that they wished every Negro in the country could be shipped to Africa. They did not believe in slavery, neither did they believe in freedom for the Negroes if the colored ones were to be allowed to mingle on an equality with the whites. At this time there were only two known slaves in the mountains, and these were regarded as two too many.

But there was another issue in the Civil War, aside from the slavery question. This issue of secession takes precedence over any other issue in the eyes of the mountain men. Fresh in memory, only yesterday on *time's* slow marching feet, independence had been won by the *united* effort of thirteen colonies. Many, therefore, bitterly opposed partition of the country. These men were Unionists.

It is not to be assumed that there was complete solidarity in the hills. Some men would rather have seen the country divided into many small republics than to see the Negroes set free; even though, as has been told, most of those did not believe in slavery as an institution. Men with this viewpoint gravitated to the Confederacy.

3

The Commonwealth of Kentucky maintained an official state of neutrality. But, within its borders, three divisions formed: (1) the Unionists (2) the Confederates or Rebels, and (3) the guerrillas.

From these three opposing forces sprang the hatreds which spawned the feuds which ran rampant for many years and painted the mountain section red; the kind of ammunition the yellow journalists and their parents, the yellow sheets of the metropolitan areas, cherished and made all efforts to acquire.

Chapter II

Settlement of Wrights and Bates

Certain names will be ever recurring throughout this book. Especially so will be these names: John W. Wright, James Claybourne Jones, Talton Hall, and Dr. M. B. Taylor. These men were the founding characters in John Fox's *Trail of the Lonesome Pine*. Not only did they make feud history, they *lived* it.

Mountaineer John Wright was known as "Bad" John to some, and "Devil" John to others. If he was known as "Angel" John to anyone, such has never been recorded.

However, feudist and savage though he may have been at times, John Wright was a man who was intensely human, subject to the emotions of any member of "homo sapiens." While his every action could not be condoned, still John Wright was a man not impossible to understand.

John was a descendant of rugged stock, his father being a man of full Irish descent who joined the great tide of westward movement, to settle upon the Boone Fork of Kentucky River about 1808, when trails had barely been broken. In fact, that fork of the river had been given its name in honor of the great pioneer leader who explored that section and camped upon its waters.

John's father, Joel Wright, came to the Kentucky

5

region from Washington County, Virginia. His nearest neighbor was John Bates, an Irishman from North Carolina, who settled seven miles below Joel Wright, at the forks of Kentucky River.

There was not a house between these two settlers. Game and fish were abundant on every hand, while the fertile valley was covered with virgin forest.

The two men set to work: clearing away the trees, planting grain, building log homes, and fencing areas for their stock and poultry. The animal pens were necessary to prevent slaughter of the stock by bears, wolves, and other wild predators.

Wright was poor and could acquire only a small boundary of land to develop. But Bates was a man of means who accumulated a vast acreage of land and timber. The business relations of these two pioneer settlers were very amicable, but when young Joel, son of the elder Joel Wright, fell in love with Bates's daughter, Eliza, a line was drawn by the Bates family.

But the line was not strong enough to hold the lovers apart. They were of age and capable, they thought, to make their own decisions. The girl chose Wright and apparent poverty.

When the marriage was a *fait accompli*, Bates bowed to the inevitable as gracefully as his pride would permit, and gave his daughter a horse. Also, he allowed the young couple to live on his land, one mile up Kentucky River from his home.

For seven years young Joel Wright and Eliza lived in a little log cabin, raising crops and paying Bates one third of the harvest as rent. At this place Solomon was born. Then came John, April 17, 1842. Later Jesse, Martin, and Sam, the other three brothers, and Sally and Susan were born to this union.

At the end of the seventh year, Joel and Eliza Wright were tired of living upon the property of another, and

6

Double log cabin of type common
during Wright's boyhood.

having to pay rent. So they fell upon a plan. Eliza sold
her horse—now growing old for horses—for fifty acres of
land two miles farther up the river. Joel erected a small
log house.

By hard work they were able to expand, to raise more
each year, to save more money. Extra garments were
made and sold, more cattle and sheep changed hands,
and the family purse grew fatter.

Within a few years Joel Wright branched out into real
estate. First he purchased small tracts adjoining his
own. Then he bought more tracts, sometimes paying
cash, but often paying in cattle, sheep, hogs, or horses.
He began buying on the head of Boone Fork, where his
father lived, and soon owned a large boundary there.
This land was all in the heart of what was later to be the
famous Elkhorn coalfield.

Thus it turned out that the wealthy Bates, who had refused his daughter's hand to the poverty-stricken young

Joel Wright, saw the latter grow in wealth until Bates's own vast fortune was put in the background.

Meanwhile, the boy John grew and developed. He was alert and intelligent, which enabled him to watch his father's business dealings and become a shrewd trader in his own right. Also at a very tender age he learned to use the rifle and the handgun. Game was yet plentiful in the mountains, and John took his turn at hunting to provide meat for the family table.

John Wright's formal schooling consisted of but six months, however, this is not strange when one remembers that during these early years in the mountains the settlers felt little need of an education. The daily tasks were those of the farm; nor did one need to know calculus to shoot five bullets into the same hole.

As the days marched by and young John edged into manhood, he was molded and hardened by the rough life of the mountains. Three arts he learned and never discarded: *working, shooting,* and *playing*.

He seemed from boyhood to have a natural detective instinct. His gray eyes never overlooked anything of importance in the field, in the forest, or on the road. He seemed to be able to size up any situation at a glance, and could scent trouble as a hound smells out the track of a raccoon. Also, he was cool and deliberate, rarely growing over-angry.

Once, when asked why he never grew angry or frightened, John replied, "You can't do anything but get hurt when you're scared or mad."

The great black cloud rolled in and obscured the land. Now the *war* was here. A hand beckoned, and away strode Joel Wright to join the ranks of them who fought, and John stood and watched and itched to go. But at home he must stay for yet awhile, the young man with the desire to go where the guns spoke.

8

Typical Cumberland Mountain terrain in which John Wright feuded, tracked criminals and helped engineers locate vast seams of coal.

In time, Joel Wright returned from the army to spend a few days at home. But no rest for him—straightway he was called upon to track down a lawless band who were roaming the mountains. Joel Wright summoned the few law-abiding citizens who were not in the army, including older men and young boys.

After a twenty-four-hour search, the band was located, fired upon, and routed. In the skirmish, Clabe Jones was captured. This particularly pleased Joel Wright, for Jones was the alleged leader of the band.

Joel Wright took Jones to his home to keep under guard until Wright was ready to return to service, three days later. Jones was permitted the freedom of the Wright home, but an eye was always upon him. When the elder Wright was otherwise occupied, he detailed his son, John, to watch the prisoner.

Then, just one day before he was to leave, Joel Wright became lax in his vigilance, and Jones escaped into the woods. Joel Wright emptied two pistols in Clabe Jones's wake, but futilely. John, by chance, was nearby. He had no gun, however, and watched helplessly. Now he pleaded with his father—again—to allow him to enlist. His father persuaded the boy that he should remain at home until the father's enlistment expired, the coming spring.

The next morning, Joel Wright returned to his headquarters in Virginia.

John Wright harnessed his horse and went to the field to gather corn. But with every step the horse made, John wished that he were free of family obligations so that he could go to Whitesburg, nearby, where, he had heard, Captain E. A. Webb was mustering a company of Confederates.

Working, sweating, wishing, John wore the day away until nearly noon, when suddenly there in the field with him stood Clabe Jones, the broad-shouldered, heavily-built escaped prisoner! Jones put one hand on the horse's bridle and his other hand on his pistol.

"Take off them gears!" Jones commanded.

"You make me!" the young man retorted.

"You little rat. I said *take them gears off!*"

"And I said, *you make me!*"

Clabe Jones slowly pulled his pistol from holster, a gleam of fury in his eyes. He pointed the muzzle toward the boy.

"Gonna take off them—"

"*No!*"

Jones stood irresolute momentarily. Then he replaced his gun in holster and himself stripped harness from John's horse. John watched in silence.

In silence, too, John Wright stood and watched Jones ride away. Then he wheeled, and strode grimly to his home. And there he learned that Jones had visited the Wright establishment and left after an argument early that morning.

And so, after all, John Wright, seething but grimly silent, journeyed to Whitesburg and became a soldier in Captain Webb's company. This was a part of the Tenth Kentucky Regiment. (Special note: John Wright understood this to be the Tenth Kentucky Regiment, but the War Department at Washington reports this to have been the Thirteenth Kentucky Regiment. This is a minor discrepancy, and it is noted purely in the interest of accuracy.)

Young John fitted easily into the life of the Confederate army. Being already a capable rifleman, horseman, and hunter, he took part in many raiding parties.

In fact, John Wright had just returned from a raid when he saved the life of Talton Hall and affected his own life's history to a far greater extent than he would ever have dreamed.

11

This happened at the home of John's uncle, at the forks of Boone and the North Fork of Kentucky River, where the group had stopped to get breakfast. Suddenly they were informed of the approach of another detachment of Confederate soldiers. When the column drew near, it was apparent that they had two prisoners in charge.

John Wright burst through his companions and hurried to meet the oncoming Confederates. Captain John T. Williams rode in front of his men. The prisoners were riding behind the saddles of two soldiers. One was a rather young man, apparently John Wright's age, very fair complexion and with slightly reddish hair. The other was nearing fifty, tall, with black hair.

"Captain, what are you doing with the prisoners?" John asked.

"Kill them unless they can prove their innocence," Captain Williams answered, eyes narrowed.

"What have they done?" John Wright wanted to know.

"Plenty. Bushwhackers, rogues, murderers—"

"That's a lie!" John interrupted.

"Just a minute, young man," Williams said calmly, as he dismounted. "Are you calling *me* a liar?"

"No," John Wright hastened to explain. "But whoever told you them things lied. I know these men. They're friends of my pa. Where'd you get your information?"

Captain Williams told him.

"Uh-huh!" John Wright said, his gray eyes widening. "Just like I thought. You got it from Clabe Jones or some of his men. Listen, captain—." Briefly he gave the captain some of Jones's background, then pleaded:

"Turn these men over to me, captain. I'll take Talt Hall with me, and he'll join the Confederate army, a member of my company. Won't you, Talt?"

Talt Hall answered quickly, agreeing.

12

"And you'll go back home and work and help the South, won't you, Harrison?" John asked Harrison Hall, Talt's uncle.

"Yeah, I sure will," Hall answered, nodding his head meanwhile.

Five minutes earlier, Harrison and Talton Hall were ready to face a firing squad. Now, Captain Williams ordered his men to turn the prisoners over to John Wright.

This gave John Wright new hope and inspiration. It was one of the great lifts in his life. He had saved, he truly believed, two innocent men from death, and had added a good soldier to the Southern cause, and another to the ranks of the citizens at home. But if the young man had known then what the man whose life he had saved would turn out to be—would he have done it?

Talt Hall enlisted and became a bosom friend of John Wright.

In the spring of 1863, Captain E. A. Webb's company was transferred to the regimental headquarters at Wise, Virginia, then called Gladeville. The outlaw band in the Kentucky River section had been quelled by the incessant raiding by soldiers. Many of them had been captured or killed. Others had escaped across Pine Mountain, into Wise and Dickenson counties, Virginia, and there had joined the already formidable band operating in that area.

Clabe Jones, it had been reported, had joined a company of the Union army, the Harlan Battalion. But John Wright hoped that he had escaped into Virginia and that they might meet there before the war ended.

Colonel Ben Caudill commanded the Confederate unit at Wise. The encampment was on a beautiful rolling hill on the outskirts of the town.

Throughout the year 1863, John Wright was never idle. His quick wit, power of intuition, his daring and fearlessness won him distinction from the start, when he

13

was chasing outlaw bands over the mountains of Letcher and other terrorized mountain communities. Now, he was being recognized upon the battlefields. As the scattered regiments of the Confederate army maneuvered up and down the borders of Kentucky, Virginia, and Tennessee, winning here, losing there, it was necessary to have messengers who could deliver the messages, otherwise whole regiments might be wiped out.

That messenger was John Wright.

To go through the enemy's own lines and reach another company of his own required not only courage and daring, but skill of the highest sort. Remember "Melissa" in *Little Shepherd of Kingdom Come*? John Fox had Melissa carry a message through the enemy lines at Cumberland Gap to save the life of "Chad." She took a cowbell and went around the face of the mountain, ringing the bell until she had gone out of hearing of the sentinels, finally delivering the message to Chad's own men. There is no question but that Fox got this inspiration from John Wright's methods of outwitting his enemies. Wright did exactly this, not once, but many times, carrying messages safely through without ever being caught.

On all occasions, where possible, he rode his wild horse, whom he called "Carnagie Bill." This horse didn't run— he flew. The trouble with Carnagie Bill was, whenever a battle came up, he considered he was already licked and "flew" for safety, unless John exerted quite an influence over him through the medium of two long spurs. John Wright never failed to make his trips in record time, yet never injured his horse.

14

Chapter III

Battle of Cynthiana, Kentucky

From Colonel Caudill's command at Wise, John Wright went to units of greater speed and activity. After surviving the great slaughter at Memphis, with Forrest, he was transferred to Colonel Giltner's command under General John Hunt Morgan.

General Morgan left Tennessee in the first of June 1864, proceeding to Lexington and adjacent points. On the morning of June 12, came the battle at Cynthiana, Kentucky. Colonel Giltner's men were eating breakfast, boasting of their successes of the day before, when the Federals opened fire on them. Barefoot men, men with mouthfuls of food, half clothed, sprang for their arms, leaving smoking food for the bluecoats soon to consume.

In the encounter, John Wright suffered a shotgun wound in the thigh.

Somehow, he escaped, fled into the countryside, and was taken in by a friendly farmer.

For thirteen days he was nursed and cared for; thirteen days he was never to forget. During that time he was nursed by one who knew how to please him; one who, somehow, knew him as no one else had ever known him. Her brown, sympathetic eyes watched over him, and the

15

patient, pleasing disposition of the girl whom they called Martha—these were to live with him throughout his life.

Martha Humphrey would come each day, bring him delicious food, dress his wound, and provide—from where, he knew not—the medicines he needed desperately. When he was able to leave, John Wright felt something he had never felt before, a tugging at his heart, a heart that had been hardened by the war and the duties he knew he must perform. He looked long at Martha and, for the first time, took her hand into his own strong one.

"Martha—I'll return. Some day, when this hellish war is over, I'll return—"

Leaving the words suspended, he strode quickly out of the room, and to the horse the farmer had ready for him.

He traveled during the night and lay up through the daylight hours, until he reached Confederate country again.

On the first day of July 1864, John Wright rode proudly into Blountville, Tennessee, and reported to his company. The flesh wounds had healed rapidly and he was almost well when he arrived.

It was apparent at that time, to all observing people, that the Southern cause was lost.

About the middle of July 1864, John Wright's headquarters received word that there were some Confederate men down in the Bluegrass section of the state who desired to enlist in the Southern army. Some of these had never yet enlisted and some had been captured by the Unionists and had escaped.

John Wright was detailed to lead a small squad to the Lexington area and bring the inquiring men through to Tennessee. Perhaps, John thought with pounding heart, he might get to see Martha again!

Talt Hall was chosen as one of Wright's men, along with seven others. Some of these men lived in the Bluegrass. When they arrived near their homes, they desired to slip

16

in to their families for a brief visit. John Wright objected to this procedure, fearing that it might lead, in some way, to the capture of the whole group. However, he could not outtalk six other men. And, too, his sympathies were with men who had been away from home for months.

Six of the men were allowed to go, while John, Talt Hall, and another were to wait for their return. Meanwhile, the released men promised to inform the leader of the would-be volunteers and have him bring his men to a certain place, near there, on the next evening, just at dark. Then all of them would begin their return trip to Tennesee.

John Wright and his two remaining companions lay in the open that night. The next morning they prepared their breakfast in a little deserted plank house. Then, taking their lunches with them, they retreated to cover, in the woods, where they remained until time to get to the appointed place at dark.

The meeting place was at the home of a supposed Confederate sympathizer, who lived faraway from anyone. He was a poor man, a renter. Small timber grew up close to the little home on one side and there was an old field on the other. A few flowers grew on each side of the rock walk from the gate to the house.

The three men rode up silently to the gate. An oil lamp flooded the house with its yellow glow. Silence prevailed, not even the rattle of a dish, for which the three listened anxiously.

"Hello!" John Wright called in a low tone.

A tall man filled the doorway, silhouetted against the yellow light.

"What will you have?" the tall man asked.

"We're looking for some men. Have you seen 'em yet?" John asked.

Suddenly Yankees came from everywhere—from the woods behind the house, from the fence around the bottom and even from behind the flower bushes.

17

All three spurred their horses and started, lying flat on the horses' backs. John was in front, now lying on the side of his horse opposite the Yankees, who were close behind. But Talt Hall and the other Rebel had been too slow. A Yankee caught Talt's horse's bridle, while another one pulled him from the saddle. Two more did the other Confederate likewise.

But John was gone. He had saved himself by a split second. He had felt the wind from the slugs that passed his ears.

However, he had not gone far when he spied men on either side of the road, as they shifted from out of the moonlight into some bushes.

He stopped quickly, turning his horse to come back down the highway.

"Halt!" Yankees everywhere!

Like a flash he sprang from the horse and sought cover in the woods. The moon shone brightly out in the open but the heavy timber obscured the light so that the Unionists could not get aim on him. As he flitted from tree to tree, slugs of lead whizzed by him, cutting the leaves close his head. But once in the bushes he was at home. No Yankee was woodsman enough to get him.

When he was safely out of their reach, he heard them cursing all Rebels in general and him in particular.

Throughout that night he traveled, venturing in, the next morning, at a little house where he got breakfast and a kindly smile. But he knew not how to take that smile. He had been betrayed on the day before. It might occur again. So he told them he was a Union soldier, hunting for an escaped prisoner. They didn't take that well. Then he knew they were Confederate sympathizers, at least.

After eating and resting a few minutes he went on, thanking his kindly hosts for their hospitality.

About nine o'clock he came to the top of a small mountain, wooded and pretty. He was almost exhausted and ready to fall asleep. So he lay down for a rest. Soon he fell asleep, notwithstanding his efforts to stay awake. But his sleep was not deep and relaxing, but rather a semi-sleep, during which almost any noise would wake him.

An hour later he was awakened by the barking of dogs. He rose and listened.

"Hounds!" he said aloud. "Fox hunters?"

No. They didn't sound like foxhounds. Anyway, who would be fox hunting in July? Or coon hunting. Then he knew, and exclaimed,

"Bloodhounds!"

That was it. He had heard of those bloodhounds which they had down in the Bluegrass to hunt men with.

Well, a *man* may get me, but no *dog* will! he thought. Where I live, dogs are used to catch animals. Men fight it out and the best one wins. If one gets away and the others can't catch him, he's just licked 'em, that's all. But here, men ain't got the brains to catch a man, but use dogs for brains.

He hurried to the top of the spur above him, where there was a small cliff. Here he arranged an opening through which he could shoot. He had only four cartridges left and he must not miss. Then he waited for the coming of the dogs, which came closer by the minute. Their loud, coarse voices resounded over the valley, reminding him of coon hunting, a sport he loved.

Now he could see the dogs. A Yankee soldier was holding to each by a long chain. They came up to where he had lain. He could hear the Union men talking, but could not tell what they were saying. They came on, finding every track he had made.

As he went up the spur he walked an old log, so that the dogs would walk it too. Now they were approaching the log.

"Boo-woo-woooo!" the front one yelped when he came to

the end of the log, then he climbed upon it, followed by the other dog.

John Wright could see the dogs' nostrils puff out and in as they smelled his tracks. The Yankees walked alongside the log, carelessly.

When the dogs were about the middle of the log, John drew aim at the front one and fired, then quickly fired at the other. Both pitched off into the green weeds, rolling and kicking, but making sounds. The soldiers, quickly glancing to his covert, fell behind the log, out of his sight.

He had but two more cartridges left. The soldiers would likely lie there for some time, afraid to stick their heads up. John took advantage of his opportunity and fled down the other side of the slope.

He ran for a mile, until he came to the edge of the woodland. Here he stopped and surveyed the surroundings. Just below him was a house where an elderly man was chopping wood in the yard. On beyond that were other houses and he could see persons here and there. Behind him were soldiers, on his trail. Maybe those in front were Yankees, too, or at least Union in sympathy, who would capture him. He meditated awhile. After all, he was tired of this hellish conflict, this continual slaughter of humanity, of wearing his own body out going from place to place, his mission being—kill, kill, kill! In a few minutes the whole future changed before him. All hopes of the success of the Confederacy fled from him. He had lost all his companions and was there, surrounded on every side by hostile foes. What would he do?

He could go on as he had come that far—fighting men and dogs—but the chances were he would get killed before he went much farther. He loved life, after all. Since he had served in the South to the best of his ability and had lost— for the South had lost—the sensible thing now to do was to give up to his enemies. Maybe when the war was over, which would be soon, he could return to his native mountains and plan his own future.

Then, looking about him, he saw a large beech tree. He walked to it and deposited both of his pistols in it. They could take him but not his guns.

Then he walked slowly down to where the old gentleman was chopping wood.

"Any Yanks around here?" he asked calmly.

"Nothin' else'd be safe here, young man" the old one answered, meanwhile sizing up John Wright from head to foot and back again.

"Yes, I know," John said, smiling disarmingly.

"An' you're a Rebel?" the white-haired man asked contemptuously.

"I was a Rebel," John admitted. "But I've stopped rebelling."

"Uh," the old man said, eyeing John closely. "An' what're you doin' here?"

"I've come to ask a favor of you."

"You, a Rebel, ask a favor of me, a Union man? What—"

"Send someone back over that hill and tell them two Yankees that I'm waiting for them here," John interrupted.

"What? You want to be a Yankee?"

"No. I want to go to jail. I think I'll be safer there."

"Uh." The elderly man adjusted his long mustache, after spitting. "Are you playin' square, young man?"

"No, I don't think I'm playing exactly square, Uncle. If I was, I'd fight the Yankees till they killed me. But I'd like to live after this devilish war's over. I've made up my mind to let 'em take me."

The hardened face of the woodchopper softened at these words and he started to call another house below when John, who had spied the two Union soldiers at the edge of the woods, stopped him.

"Tell 'em to come on, that I ain't got no arms," John re-

21

quested. Meanwhile, he threw back his coat, showing that he had no guns on him.

John's host, for now he might be so-called, told the soldiers that John had given up and for them to come and get him.

Notwithstanding John had killed their dogs, the Yankees treated him kindly on their way back to Lexington, where he was placed in prison.

Here he found Talt Hall and his other friend he had lost at the little house.

"What're you doing here?" John asked Talt Hall.

"An' what're you?" Talt asked sullenly—a trait for which he was noted.

"Oh, I just came in to see how the Yankees live," John joked.

"Yanks h—!" Hall exploded angrily. "You'll find out how the *Rebels* live."

"Well, there's no use to cry," John suggested. "There'll be brighter days."

The guards and officers told them: "The last ray of hope for the South has already gone. Those who take the oath of allegiance to the Union will be treated well. You men can have your freedom, under certain conditions, of course, if you obey your oath."

It was a great decision for John Wright to make. He and Talt Hall had fought together through the years of war and hardship. They had been taught, and they sincerely believed, that they were fighting for a just cause, and had been encouraged to fight to the bitter end, rather than submit to the tyranny of the North. In their hearts they were still Rebels, yet *Southerners.* They would remain Rebels, no matter where they were sent, or what was forced upon them.

However, a few weeks in prison wrought a change in John Wright's and Talt Hall's minds. At last they came to realize that the sensible thing to do was to take the oath of

22

allegiance to the country in which they lived. They signed the oath and were taken to Cincinnati and turned loose, after being instructed not to leave the state of Ohio. If they should disobey their oaths, death might be the penalty.

When they were given their freedom at Columbus, Ohio, months later, the two young men started for their own Kentucky mountains. They walked to the Ohio River at Portsmouth. From there, they rode a boat to Catlettsburg, at the mouth of Big Sandy River. Big Sandy was at low tide, so boats could not ply above Louisa, some thirty miles upstream. At Louisa, they hired a man to take them on horses to Prestonsburg, from which point they rode other horses to the forks of Beaver Creek, where the thriving city of Martin, in Floyd County, now stands. At Martin, they separated. Talt started his long trek up the Right Beaver Valley, into Knott County, while John Wright hurried up Left Beaver, toward Letcher County and the upper Kentucky River section.

When John reached the top of the mountain dividing the Beaver valleys and Kentucky River, the huge bulk of Pine Mountain loomed welcomingly in the distance. Its high peaks and low passes, corrugating the sky, seemed to welcome him home. Here he had been born and reared, fished, and hunted—for beast and man.

He was happy to be home again. However, there was a depressing feeling, something which told him that things would not be as they were when he had left three years ago.

As he passed the scenes he knew so well, observing heaps of ashes where once had stood peaceful homes, deserted cabins, half torn away by the hands of outlaws, or by opposing sides in the war, he longed for the return of happy days again.

He went not to his home, for he was informed that his father had moved to Virginia long ago, to escape the

23

ravaging hands of the guerrillas. He desired not to look upon the lonely place, but went about inquiring for the boys with whom he had played and hunted before the war. Most of these had been killed or had left the country, he was told. But not being a young man disposed to brood over the past, John Wright pulled himself together and started for Scott County, Virginia, to find his father and mother.

He passed through Pound Gap, where history says (then) Col. James A. Garfield defeated Gen. Humphrey Marshall in the spring of 1862, during an early morning snowstorm. John Wright contended throughout his life that there never had been a battle at Pound Gap; that there was a small skirmish one time, resulting in a rout of the Federals. However, since Wright had fought with Colonel Caudill, Forrest, Giltner, and John Hunt Morgan, he might have been far away when Garfield invaded Marshall's quarters there.

When John found his father and mother, in Scott County, Virginia, and heard them tell of the woeful tales of atrocities and their escape, he had difficulty keeping back tears. But few tears had ever escaped his eyes. Having been reared in the primitive years, he had known nothing but to take life as it came, bitter and sweet, and to work or fight, as the occasion demanded, but never finding time to weep.

Wagons, drawn by oxen, hauled the Wright belongings back to their home on Kentucky River.

It was late spring, but John Wright, his father, and brothers put up fence, grubbed and plowed the fields and planted them in record time. Fencings and corn hoeings were resumed, and the spirit of cooperation, of brotherhood, returned to the valleys.

However, as soon as the crop was well finished, John Wright grew restless. The years of traveling, of excitement, hunting men and being hunted, had wrought in him a rambling urge. He wanted to see more of the world, more people; he wanted to learn, to earn money, go well dressed. The mountains had lost their lure.

Chapter IV

Sees World With John Robinson Circus

Martin Van Buren Bates was one of the world's wonders. He was a brother of John Wright's mother, and was seven years older than John. Bates remained a normal child until he had passed his seventh birthday. Then he began to grow so fast that his mother would not make him work. At the age of thirteen he weighed three hundred pounds.

Bates had gone through the war, ranking as captain when the conflict ended. He had grown and developed now, at the age of twenty-eight, until he tipped the scale around five hundred and measured seven feet and eleven inches in his stockings.

Bates, like John Wright, had acquired the wanderlust during the hectic war years. He planned to leave the mountains, never to return. He desired a companion, and knowing none better than John Wright, his nephew, he offered to take him and help him find work. John gladly accepted and the two made their way over mountains and streams, over the rolling plains of the Bluegrass, until they came to Cincinnati.

Here they found a small show, known as the Wiggins and Bennoitt, exhibiting. Bates approached the manager

Captain and Mrs. Martin Van Buren Bates posed with an average-size man. Captain Bates was John Wright's uncle. The captain's standing height was seven foot eleven inches. Mrs. Bates was eight foot even.

and was at once hired at one hundred dollars a month, and John Wright put to work at fifty dollars a month.

They went with this show for a few months but were not

happy. It did not travel far enough, nor was their pay large enough. They returned to Cincinnati at a time when they were informed that the John Robinson Circus would be showing there. They found Robinson's show exhibiting. Bates was given *four hundred dollars* a month, and John Wright one hundred dollars.

Months of excitement and romance followed. Every week there were new faces, strange places, and unfamiliar scenes. Money jingled in their pockets, nice clothes covered their forms, and delicious meals were always at their command.

During the second summer the circus made a trip through Nova Scotia. Here Bates met his wife-to-be, Miss Anna Hannon Swan, a woman eight feet tall, one inch taller than the giant himself. But she weighed slightly less than he.

The circus hired Miss Swan and she and Bates were the wonder of the show.

Within a few months the Robinson circus went to London, England, to exhibit. The crossing of the Atlantic and landing in a foreign country were all thrilling to these Kentucky mountain men.

While the show was performing in London, Queen Victoria attended it. Upon sight of the two enormously-proportioned persons, she was amazed. At once she made their acquaintance. Nothing had ever been seen in England to compare with these marvelous people!

The queen wanted to show her appreciation for the sight, and so she had each of them a watch made in proportion to their size. Bates's watch was as large as an ordinary saucer, resembling an alarm clock, with luminous dial. Miss Swan's watch was almost as large. Each was valued at one thousand dollars.

Bates, who had acquired the title, "Kentucky Giant," and Miss Swan decided that nature had placed them on

Old-time circus similar to the one John Wright toured the country with, in company with his uncle Martin Bates.

the earth, the one for the other, since there were none like them. They were married in London.

For years they remained with the show, at large salaries, and saved a fortune.

When they left the show, they settled in Seville, Ohio. Here, they lived until the death of the large woman.

The following article was published in the *Big Sandy News*, a weekly newspaper, of Louisa, Kentucky, home of the late Fred Vinson, former chief justice of the United States. It was dated June 10, 1910:

GIANT BATES

Among the freaks of the old days who have retired with competence is Martin Van Buren Bates, the Kentucky giant, now sixty-three (should be seventy-three) years of age, who is spending the fag end of a long and picturesque career on a little farm near Seville, Ohio. Captain Bates, renowned throughout Europe and America for many years for his unusual size. His romantic marriage while entour to Anna K. Shaw (Anna Hannon Swan), the Canadian giantress, a woman one inch taller than himself was a nine days wonder at the time. Mrs. Bates died several years ago, leaving no issue. One child had been born to her but it died in infancy. Cpt. Bates is still hale and hearty (in 1910). One of his principal pleasures now is a discussion of the causes which led up to the conflict between the States, in which resort to arms he participated as a lad.

Captain Bates was born in Letcher County in 1847 (1837). Unusually large (ordinary) at his birth, he measured six feet in height and weighed 170 pounds on his eleventh birthday. At twenty-one he measured seven feet and eleven inches in his stockings, and weighed 400 pounds. He tipped the scales at 500 (525) while in his prime. Unlike the usual giant, Capt. Bates never suffered from a week spinal column and his muscles are not atrophied. In fact he was noted for his agility and strength during and after the Civil War. His parents were plain people of ordinary size. The other children born to the couple were normal. Capt. Bates had three brothers, the combined weight of whom did not much exceed his own.

Bates cast his lot with the young Confederacy at the outbreak of the Civil War, becoming a private in the Third Kentucky Infantry. He was at that time only fourteen (twenty-four) years of age, but was more than a man in stature. At sixteen (26) he was

30

promoted to be a captain for bravery exhibited on the field of battle. He distinguished himself in the several engagements in which he participated. He was severly wounded in one of the battles around Cumberland Gap.

In 1870 Capt. Bates made a tour of England and the Continent where he was exhibited to enthusiastic crowds.

After his marriage Capt. Bates purchased the farm, and erected the house near Seville, Ohio, where he still lives (1910). The measurements of this house were made commensurate with the unusual proportions of the people who were to live in it. The bed on which the couple slept measured ten feet in length with a width in proportion and was of a height twice that of an average bed. A magnificent dressing table constructed for the use of Mrs. Bates contained a mirror almost as large as the side of an ordinary house.

It was a novel sight to see the giant and his wife out for a drive. The carriage in which they rode was a huge affair. The wheels reached almost to the second story of an average house, and six stout horses were used to draw it.

Capt. Bates married again some years after the death of his first wife. His second wife is a woman of ordinary size, who looks like a pigma beside her giant husband. They reside at the Captain's old home, where he is passing the life of a gentleman of leisure.

The reading of the above, taken from a recent number of the Paintsville Herald, reminds the News of a couple of visits made to Louisa by Baby Bates. The first call was an involuntary one. As the Herald says, Bates cast his lot with the Confederacy, but he was more than fourteen years old when he enlisted, and he must be at least 68 (73) years old now. The occasion of that first visit to Louisa was when he as a prisoner of war was taken through this town enroute to Camp Chase, Ohio. He, with many others of Humphrey Marshall's command, was captured on the raid through Pound Gap. He made this grand entry into Louisa on board a little army mule, and it is said that the Baby's feet swept the ground as he rode along. His next visit was in March, 1867. He had been all over the United States and a good part of Europe and was going home to Letcher County via water to Pikeville and overland to his native county. When his boat reached this point—it must have been the Red Buck—the river was too high to admit further travel by water, and Bates left the boat and went to the hotel to await a fall of the stream. Uncle Tip Moore was then keeping hotel in the old Moore brick at the head of the grade, and there the giant remained until the boat could proceed on its journey. Of course he attracted a great deal of attention, as well he might. He was the biggest man, so the News ventures to assert, that the world ever saw. There have been men who weighed more, but they were masses of flesh without corresponding height. Bates lacked only an inch of being eight feet high in his stockinged feet. He was admirably proportioned, hands and feet matched to such enormous weight and height. When here on his second visit, he weighed 525 pounds. One day while sitting in a room with white washed walls at the hotel he was leaning back in his chair with one foot encased in a heavy boot flat against the wall. A bystander saw the chance, and asking Bates to hold still a minute he took a lead pencil and marked on the wall an outline of the "Baby's" pedal extremity, and that drawing remained there many a day thereafter. When taking his infrequent strolls through Louisa Bates always wore a pair of yellow kid gloves, making his hands resemble a pair of canvassed hams.

The big fellow was in Louisa several days, and during that time he paid two or three visits to the Masonic Academy. He showed great interest in boys and girls and they returned it many fold. The principal would often purposely stand as close to Bates as possible, and the difference between the giant's eight feet and the teacher's five feet six provoked many a laugh. Bates was a man of much refinement, quiet and gentlemanly in his deportment. He was very temperate and took care of his money and his presents, which were many and valuable. One was a gold hunting case watch, gift of Queen Victoria. It was as large as a saucer, and Bates wore it, with a solid gold neck chain, made to correspond with the timepiece. He was fond of visiting at the home of Late Judge J. M. Rice, where in addition to the genial Judge and his noble wife and the fine eatin', there was a cook, a white girl nearly six feet tall and built along corresponding lines. She could—and did stand up straight under Bates' outstretched arm.

There are many living in Louisa now who remember Baby Bates (1910), and the News feels sure they are all glad to know that he is still living and is in good circumstances.

Captain Bates created quite a lot of excitement everywhere he went. There were several funny jokes told about him. One was during his service in the army. His company was surprised one night by a squad of Unionists who rushed into their sleeping quarters routing the Rebels completely.

No one had time to put his clothes on in the rush, so their garments were snatched as they went. After they had fled to a safe distance from the Yankees they stopped to don their clothes. Captain Bates, instead of getting his own pants, got those of a small man. He was found trying to get these on, in the dark.

Bates stayed seven years with the world's largest show, then retired to his specially built home at Seville, Ohio, where he spent a life of leisure—well earned.

But John Wright soon tired of the continual travel from place to place. At first he enjoyed it, but two or three years were sufficient to satisfy him that the chance to travel and see the world, to dress elegantly, to have money to spend, to be able to court the fair sex of many lands, and to eat the finest food the world afforded, did not bring him the satisfaction which he had anticipated. He longed again for the deep forests, the shaded streams, the lonely cabins, and most of all that feeling of "home," which only the mountains of his boyhood could afford him.

And so on one of the show's return trips to Cincinnati, John bade it farewell and started for his native hills.

Chapter V

Wright Returns to Cynthiana and Martha

It was in the spring of 1869 when John Wright left the
John Robinson Circus at Cincinnati, where he had joined
it following the close of the Civil War. During the past
years, he had traveled over a great portion of the world, including England. He had been observant, studying people
of all classes and in different countries. For him, it had
been a great school, more than his mountains could ever
have afforded. By listening to well-spoken, well-bred
people, he had learned much proper language and man-
ners. Whenever he heard a word spoken, which meaning
he did not know, he connected it with the other words in
the sentence and figured out the meaning. In spare hours
from his hard show routine, he studied books and, like
Lincoln, he "collared" anything he undertook. This had
been reality and action studied firsthand, and it fitted him
for the colorful and dramatic life which awaited him back
in the mountains of his boyhood.

He headed toward the mountains, walking. Uppermost
in his mind was Martha Humphrey, of Cynthiana. Martha, brown-eyed, patient, and gentle, had nursed him back
to health five years ago, when he was wounded at the battle of Cynthiana. But for her, he might not have survived.
Sometimes the events of life had crowded the Bluegrass

girl far back into the recesses of his memory, but at times, when he had a moment to meditate, she lived vividly again in his heart. Now that he was free from the worries and hard work of the show, her image loomed larger within him.

He wondered how far it was to Cynthiana, as he hurried along the pike from the twin cities of Covington and Newport, Kentucky. He longed for his native homeland, his kin and friends, after several years. Yet, something about the girl he carried in his breast shoved these things into the background. There had been the little romance with the Indian chief's daughter, but that had soon been forgotten. But Martha—she clung to him more tightly as Cincinnati became more vague behind him.

But, maybe she was married, John thought. Or, maybe she has passed on—. He cut the thought short. Such as Martha Humphrey could never die.

Presently he met a man who drove cattle and sheep. The man rode a high-headed, prancing horse, dark bay with white face. The man was fat, with square face, florid cheeks, his second chin protruding beyond the first.

When John approached close he saw the drover held some attraction for him.

"Nice pigs you got there," John said. "Taking them to market?"

"Yes," the other replied, not unfriendly. "You seem to know something about hogs."

"I know to eat 'em," John said, smiling up at the man in the saddle.

"What do you know about cattle?" the drover asked, earnestly.

"Oh, I know how to feed 'em and milk 'em. But," he said, appraising the small group of stock, "trading them is more fun."

"I see," the rider said, but had to pause to hold his horse, which was prancing back and forth, never still a moment.

"Say, why don't you make that horse stand where you want him?" John asked.

"He's wild as fury. Don't get enough riding, I guess, or enough work."

John laughed heartily.

"Old Carnagie Bill, my horse that I rode in the war, tried to put that stuff off on me, too, but he failed. I taught him to go or stay, but to do one or the other—not both at the same time."

"Say, young man, what's your name?" The drover's eyes widened as he appraised John.

"John Wright, from the mountains. What's yours?"

"My name's Joe Bailey. By the way, you strike me as just the man I'm looking for."

"Want somebody murdered?" John asked half seriously.

"Oh, no! I need a good man to help me on my farm and in my trading."

"Where's your farm?"

"Near Cynthiana, oh about—"

"You live at Cynthiana?"

"Sure. Why?"

John Wright sighed deeply, meditating. Should he ask the man about Martha? Maybe she—

"Why do you ask that?" the drover insisted.

"Do you know Martha Humphrey?" he asked, at last, holding his breath for the answer.

"Martha Humphrey? One of the finest young women in the Bluegrass. Do *you* know her?"

"Is she—still single?" John asked, ignoring the other's question.

"Sure, she's single. And, from her actions, she'll stay single until death. She won't look at a man. Tell me what you know about Martha."

John told him the story.

"Well, that clears up the mystery," the drover said, with apparent relief. "We all felt that Martha had a sweet-

36

heart sometime, somewhere, in her past, but no one ever knew. I suppose you're the man. She could have married the finest of men, but she has never given even one a chance."

John Wright forgot all about the mountains for the time being.

"If you'll take a job with me, you'll be close to Martha all the time," the drover said.

"It's a deal, Mr. Bailey," John agreed quickly. "But," looking the prancing horse over, "the first thing I'm going to do is stop that horse from frolicking on the highway."

"Do you think you can?"

"I'll stop him in less than a week. What's his name?"

"Joe. I named him, while a colt, after myself, my first name."

John returned to Covington with Bailey and after the cattle and hogs had been sold, they went to Cynthiana, where John, that very night, called on Martha Humphrey, the young lady whom he'd carried in his heart all these years.

She was the same Martha, except that she had developed, matured. The somewhat girlish face had now filled out, round and perfect in features, while her brown eyes had only brightened and grown larger, and more charming—if possible—since the night he had taken her hand into his own and promised that some day—when the *hellish* war was over—he would return.

But in this home, he sensed the tang of aristocracy. It was a Bluegrass home, not a mountain cabin. And there was at this time the same prejudice between these two sections, the same lack of understanding, as there was between the North and the South. The lower or favored section looked upon the inhabitants of the mountains as bloody feudists, rough backwoodsmen, ignoramuses. The mountain people looked down on them with an utter disregard, an independence, classing them as aristocrats, high-hatters, white-collars, even "furriners."

But there was none of this contemptible atmosphere about Martha Humphrey. And for that reason John Wright could bear the slurring remarks of her parents, who objected strenuously to her associating with him. Her parents were not rich, or even wealthy, yet they were not poor, as John was. They desired that she marry a man of her own caste, not a rough mountaineer.

But there was something between the two—an understanding, a point of contact, a mysterious something— which the choice of parents or the prejudice of sections could not separate. Martha had been captivated on sight by the indomitable courage, the flashing gray eyes, the lithe, trim figure, the indefinite something called personality. There was something about him, indescribable, which no other living person in her life had had.

And so during the summer, contrary to the wishes of the parents, John and Martha were married, both being of age, and able to make their choices in life.

They lived with the Humphreys during the next few months. John showed himself to be at the head of the list in anything that came his way. No one could handle horses and cattle as he could. Bailey's horse had long ago stopped his prancing. John proved to be one of the shrewdest dealers in that part of the country, and the Humphreys now agreed that Martha had chosen wisely.

In the early fall, there were to be some horse races at Cynthiana. Some of the horses which were scheduled to run came from Lexington on the day before the races were to start. These were kept in Cynthiana overnight.

Among these was one valued at one thousand dollars. The next morning when the horses were fed it was found that the fine horse was gone!

Immediately a posse, headed by the sheriff of the county, made ready to start on the thief's trail. A large crowd

38

thronged around the sheriff and his men, shouting for the capture of the horse thief who had stolen the famous race animal.

"Don't worry!" the sheriff yelled at the throng. "We'll get him."

Meanwhile the man who had brought John Wright to Cynthiana was making his way through the crowd.

"Here!" Mr. Bailey exclaimed, finally reaching the sheriff's side. "Take this man! He ain't afraid of the devil himself and he can track a horse like a beagle can track a rabbit."

The sheriff cast an indifferent eye toward the young man. The sectional chasm shone through his expression. He turned to the owner of the famous racehorse.

"Would you rather take chances on this mountain Rebel bringing back your horse, or leave him in the hands of the thief that's got him?" he asked.

John Wright straightened his tall, strong form. His eyes narrowed as he pushed his way closer to the officer. Instinctively his right hand gripped his side where seldom a revolver failed to be, but there was none there now.

"Take the young man along," the owner told the officer.

"If John Wright finds the horse and fails to bring him back, I'll stand responsible for the animal." The fast words came from Joe Bailey. "I'll beat that: He can ride my best horse, Joe."

"Take him!" came shouts from all over the crowd.

The sheriff glanced with disdain at John and said, "Well, Wright, what do you say?"

John, so far, had not spoken. Now his gray, keen eyes held the sheriff's in an unmistakable gaze.

"I say that if you hadn't been an officer of the law, one of us would have taken a licking."

The throng yelled and pressed closer.

The sheriff's face flushed and he cast quick glances over

39

the people. Seeing that sentiment was in Wright's favor, he decided to pass the matter off as a joke. His face brightened as he looked directly at John Wright, a faint smile breaking about his eyes.

"Wanta go with us?"

"Tracking down horse thieves is no poker game," John answered calmly. "I'm not raring to go. But *somebody's* got to get the man's horse. For *his* sake, I'll go."

The air was instantly full of hats and yells.

"Bet five to one that John Wright brings back the horse," wagered Joe Bailey.

The posse was divided into two's, which spread in every direction from Cynthiana. John desired to ride with the sheriff. The two and another man rode down Licking River, toward Cincinnati.

"I've got my own way of tracking horse thieves," John told the officer. "I've caught as many of them as I have jackrabbits. I'll go with you till you leave the track, then I'll leave you.

"Just so you get the horse," the officer replied.

"I've made no promises, nor did I ask your permission to go," John answered firmly. "I make no promises now. Except one. If I don't get the horse I'll be a long time gone. So don't worry about the one I'm riding."

The trio rode on for an hour, inquiring at every home. They had followed the horse's tracks for a while from Cynthiana. The toes of the rear feet dug deeply in when making a step, such as no other horses in that vicinity did. In crossing streams and passing over sand and other soft places, it was easy to follow the horse, but when they struck the hard pike it was difficult.

On a hard pike, John Wright stopped suddenly and alighted from his horse.

"Say, officer, I know what it means to track thieves. Suppose I get away off, tracking this man? I'll have to get help from somebody."

40

"We'll all be together," the sheriff explained.

"Maybe we will, and again, maybe we won't," John said, unconvinced. "In case we are separated, I want a note from you, telling that I'm deputized to catch the stealer of the race horse."

"Oh, that's nonsense," protested the officer.

"Maybe," John said. "But you give me a summons to protect me or I'll go back."

Reluctantly the officer wrote a summons, deputizing John to apprehend the thief. John remounted his horse and the three rode away.

In the middle of the afternoon, they found where the famous horse had left the pike and had cut across country, coming to the Ohio River a few miles east of Newport, Kentucky. There were the deep imprints of the horse's hind feet where he had gone into the Ohio River.

John was convinced beyond a doubt that the thief had forced the racehorse to swim the river, which was now at high stage.

"Nothing else we can do, boys," the sheriff told his men.

"Maybe not for you," John said calmly but determinedly. "But for me—there is plenty to do. Sheriff, here's where we part."

"Part?" the officer asked, apparently puzzled. "What do you mean, man?"

"I mean I'm going after that man's horse."

"But *how*?"

"Ford the river."

"What? You aim to put that horse in there and get him drowned?"

"Nope," John replied. "But this horse and I will cross the river."

"But you'll both drown and I'll be responsible," the sheriff said.

"No you won't be responsible. I'll be as good as you. I'll

41

give you writing to show that I rebelled and went on my own. I'm a Rebel, you know."

On the back of an old envelope, which he had requested of the officer, John signed the necessary release and handed it to the sheriff.

The sun was setting fast now and to the sheriff its red glows were ominous forebodings of an unpleasant sight which would soon take place before their eyes.

"Tell Martha not to look for me till she sees me coming, and tell Mr. Bailey if he never sees old Joe, to blame me," were John's last words to his companions.

He climbed into the saddle, placed his two pistols, ammunition and other things he did not want wet, in his coat pockets and folded the coat up around his neck. He reined the horse into the water.

After the first few yards, John had no trouble with the animal. He held the rein taut and gripped the pommel of the saddle, his legs pushed out from the animal's sides.

The two men stood and watched with bated breath as man and horse took a diagonal course downstream, toward the opposite side. On the horse and rider went, their forms became smaller and smaller until they looked not larger than ducks on the water.

Several minutes later, horse and rider climbed the bank far across the water. When they were away from the river's edge, John Wright waved farewell to his erstwhile companions.

A short distance from his landing, John took up at a farmhouse for the night.

Chapter VI

Long Chase Ends With Gunfight

Early the following morning, John Wright resumed his chase after the thief of the famous racehorse. He rode Old Joe again today, since the animal had not traveled far the previous day.

When darkness came upon him again, he was within a few miles of the Ohio River, near Huntington, West Virginia. Here he spent the night with a very hospitable man who gave him valuable information about the country through which he must pass.

During the night John told his host that he would need a fresh horse on the coming day. After breakfast, and still before daylight, a fast horse was ready for him. He left Mr. Bailey's Old Joe at this point pending his return—if he did return.

John tracked the racehorse to the Ohio River again just above Huntington, and swam the river, landing on the West Virginia side.

The rest of the day, he traveled through this state, never at any time having any difficulty following his man. The stolen horse was such a stately, high-headed, peppy animal, enhanced by its long, flowing mane and tail, the white triangle in the black face, and its graceful limbs and shining black hair—these attracted attention everywhere the animal was seen.

At the end of this day he was some miles closer to his man, according to information gathered along the way. He traveled until late in the night, hoping to gain more ground.

Now, since he must have a fresh horse every day if he expected to overtake the man who rode the fast racehorse, he made a point to spend the nights with families who had horses.

At dark on the third day, John Wright was assured that his man was not more than five miles ahead of him. Inspired by this hope he rode on until nearly midnight, expecting the thief to take up somewhere for the night. But, seeing that his borrowed horse was lagging, and that there was no chance of overtaking the criminal that night, he stopped for a few hours' rest.

The fourth morning he left a hospitable home, furnished with a tall, dark brown horse, full of life and eager for the reins to be released. This horse had no gaits except a gallop and a walk. Its trotting was so hard that the rider could not bear it long in succession. And so the day was spent in series of walking, trotting, and galloping, but just enough trotting to rest the horse from the fast running.

At night the rider pulled in to a farmhouse near the West Virginia-Virginia border, but in the latter state. His horse, which had not been used to hard riding, was completely exhausted.

At this point he was about three hours behind his man and was glad to stop for a night's sleep. He knew that soon the racehorse must begin to lag. In fact he knew that the horse was already near exhaustion, but was being pushed by the heartless thief.

The following morning, which was the fifth since he had left Cynthiana, he mounted a small grey horse with a high head, skittish and fearful of stumps, logs, and other objects. Sometimes there was a vigorous protest from the little horse over passing such things, but the two sharp spurs on John's heels rotated up and down the animal's sides, helping it to decide to proceed. Twice the horse became frightened and ran away, but never fast enough for John Wright.

This day had proved a diversion from the other four. John, who was becoming worn somewhat from the continuous grind, had gotten a kick out of the little horse and had a mind to ride him on the next morning. However, he feared the animal might not be able to make the speed he desired.

For two more days he followed his man over southwestern Virginia, into Tennessee, and back again into Virginia, ever gaining, but never catching him.

On the night of the seventh day, John Wright rode until late, as his information indicated that he was not more than an hour behind the thief. But both he and his horse were tired and hungry, and he must take up for the night.

For the first time since he started, he stayed with a man who had no horses.

Starting early next morning, he began searching for a fresh animal. After an hour, he rode up to a prosperous-looking farmhouse and saw the man brushing a fine black horse in the barnyard. He alighted, opened the gate and led his horse inside.

"Howdy," John said.

"Good morning," the man returned the greeting, casting an indifferent look at both the newcomer and the horse.

"Mister, I've got to swap horses with you for awhile," John informed him.

The man stopped brushing, his eyes fastened upon the youthful looking man who had ridden onto his property uninvited.

"You—*what?*"

"I'm hunting for a horse thief that's just gone this way," John explained. "I've got to have a fresh horse." His words carried a tone of demand, not request.

"Well, stranger, you don't get *this* horse," the owner declared with emphasis. Then he resumed brushing.

"Yeah, I do," John replied calmly. "This is the one I'm getting." Meanwhile, he hitched his borrowed horse and faced the big man. "You keep my horse until I return. I'll return yours in good condition. But I can't say when."

He started unsaddling his horse, but ever keeping an eye on the owner of the other.

Suddenly the man sprang from his horse and picked up a rock and started to throw it. Like a flash, John jerked a revolver, leveled it.

"Here," John said, pulling the summons from his pocket. "Read this."

After the farmer had read the paper, the hardness left his face and he relaxed.

"Well, it looks like you've won," he said, smiling wryly.

"Don't worry, mister," John soothed. "I'll be back this way if the racehorse thief don't get me. Take good care of this horse," indicating the one he'd ridden there, "for he belongs to somebody else, too."

With this, John threw his saddle on the other's horse and leaped into the saddle then speeded away.

For three hours he rode at top speed, until, at ten o'clock, he was nearing Cumberland Gap. He stopped at a small board house on the right of the road, where two men were talking in the yard.

"Howdy, fellers," John greeted.

"Howdy," one answered, uncertainly.

"See a feller ride by here on a big black horse—"

"With a three-cornered white spot in his face?" one interrupted.

"Yeah—"

46

"Jest now passed. Mebbe fifteen, twenty minutes ago."

"Riding fast?" John wanted to know.

"Jest pokin' along. Horse must a been tired."

John spurred his horse into a fast gallop for two miles.

Now, he could see Cumberland Gap, a mile ahead—that historic spot, he knew, in the corner of three states, where the floods of pioneers, including ancestors of his own father, had come across the Blue Ridge, up the Shenandoah, pushing on toward the great Kentucky wilderness.

He was at last within sight of his man. A tall rider sat erect on the famous horse, and whistled with apparent happiness and a feeling of security. The horse was walking, the reins hanging loose.

At the sound of John's coming, the leisurely rider turned quickly. But apparently he did not suspect the traveler approaching him. He resumed his whistling.

When John rode up, the man swayed over to the left of the road and John came up beside him, on the man's right, which was what John wanted—he thought. Should the man attempt to fight it out it would be harder for him to draw and shoot to the right than across the pommel of the saddle, to the left. Here, John Wright thought he scored a high point.

"Howdy," John said, smiling broadly.

"Mornin'," the tall, angular man answered, without expression of any kind.

Two large revolvers rested on the man's hips. He looked at John's horse, and the impression on his face changed instantly.

"Why you been ridin' so hard?" he asked.

"Been after a doctor for my wife," John replied without hesitation. "She's bad off."

The small, bullet eyes of the tall man expressed their disbelief.

"Whur's the doctor?" he asked.

"He'll be right along. Had to splint a broken arm before he could come."

They rode on in silence for a moment, the eyes of the tall man never for an instant leaving John, nor John's leaving him.

"Say, that's a fine horse you've got," John complimented, as if he had just now noticed it. "Where'd you get such an animal?"

The tall man's eyes flashed his disapproval of prying into his personal affairs.

"Traded for 'm," he said at last.

"Want to trade him?"

"I ain't tradin' none," with a tone of finality.

Meanwhile, John's right hand rested on the butt of the revolver on his left side, covered by the tail of his coat. He sized up the man now, really for the first time. Long-pointed mustache curved around his small mouth; a stubble of two weeks' beard covered his lean, broad face. John perceived that the man's hearing and sight were acute, and that his actions were like lightning. John Wright decided now to take no chances.

"Iff'n your wife's so porely, why ain't you goin' to 'er?' the man asked, eyeing John closely.

"Can't you see my horse is worn out?"

"Yeah—I see."

"Listen, Mister, I want to trade for that horse," John bantered. "I've got money to pay the difference."

"Didn't I tell you I ain't tradin' none?"

John pulled his reins and stopped.

"But if you'd get down and look mine over you might change your mind," he said.

The thief had stopped simultaneously with John's movements.

"Say—what'n—h—you tryin' to pull?" The tall man's left hand was near the butt of the revolver on his right side and John watched every movement.

48

"Well, I've come a long way to get that horse. If you must know—"

At this point the thief's left hand seized the revolver on the right side, while John's right hand swung his into action. As John ducked over the side of his horse, there was a burning sensation right on top of the head. The horse stealer was left-handed!

Meanwhile, the thief had swung off his horse on the opposite side. But John, knowing that if he dropped to the ground, his opponent would shoot him in the lower parts and if he straightened up on his horse, he would be shot in the head.

For the few seconds he hung to the pommel of the saddle with his left hand, his foot in the stirrup, his mind worked as it never had worked before. He had nowhere to go! Each second was an eternity until he thought of the course he must take.

Sticking his revolver down under the horse's belly, he aimed as nearly as possible and fired, though not seeing his object, but judging from the way the horses were standing.

For the brief second, during which John waited for a return fire, there was deathly silence, then he heard staggering steps, followed by a thud on the ground.

Confident that he had gotten his foe, John dropped to the ground and saw the tall figure lying, his head near the racehorse's front feet.

John peered over his horse's neck, fearing another shot from his opponent. The latter was weakly raising his gun, aiming it at John's head. But he was too late. A second shot from John's revolver finished the man and finished John Wright's long and exhausting chase over five states.

John examined his victim. The first shot had entered low in the abdomen. The second had hit center between the eyes. Although it had been a case of kill or die, it was a gruesome sight and young Wright, for a moment, regretted that he had not obeyed the sheriff's orders and gone back with him. However, these thoughts were only momentary. He had acted in line of duty and in the execution of the law, for the welfare of man and country.

Then John began to relieve his victim of the latter's personal belongings. A new Colt's .38 revolver was taken from the strong grip of the man's left hand, the lock half drawn back by the deathly grip. From the holster he pulled another, just like the first, but older. He worked these and found that they had been well cared for and were in perfect condition.

Then he searched the pockets, hoping that he might find something that would identify the thief.

What's this? A roll of something tied in a bandanna handkerchief. Greenback! Yellow twenties, green twenties, tens, fives—over seven hundred dollars!

He shoved the roll into his pocket and finished the search.

John's next thought was the burial of the body. He looked about for a house and saw a small cabin close. Mounting his horse, he rode to the gate and called. A little gray-haired man came to the door.

"Uncle, a man's had trouble up on the road. I want you to come and help him."

"Yessum, in a minute," and he shuffled back into the house, returning in seconds, making short, rapid steps.

When the little man saw what had happened, he turned pale, his eyes widening.

"Murdered!"

"Not murdered," John explained. "He just got the worst of a fight, Uncle."

"I can't help *him*. He's dead."

"Yes, you can help him," John said, as he pulled out the roll of currency. He handed the little man a twenty dollar bill. "Bury him."

The old man looked for a moment at the money, then with a trembling hand, took it, stuck it into his pocket.

"I think you orta gimme one of them guns," the native said, pleadingly, as he eyed both of the dead thief's revolvers.

"Of course I'll give you one," John agreed. "But be careful you don't shoot yourself with it." Then John handed him the older gun, and some cartridges.

John Wright then began his long trip back to Cynthiana. If he could have come from Cumberland Gap down the old Wilderness Trail, hundreds of miles could have been saved. But he had to retrace his steps all the way back in order to deliver the "borrowed" horses to their owners.

He arrived at the home where he got the last horse just at lunchtime—to John Wright, it was dinner time. He had entertained no hope of receiving a welcome here, since the man had attempted to fight him because he took his horse. But when he rode into the barnyard and hitched up the horse and the racehorse, the man came out onto the porch and called to him:

"Hey—dinner's ready! Come and eat with us."

"Coming," John answered.

The farmer apologized to him for his rash act and offered him the best they had to eat.

"No offense," John assured him. "I knew you didn't understand."

Immediately after the meal, John climbed onto the "next" man's horse and led the racehorse away on the long journey home.

Twelve days were spent in returning. He let the racehorse rest two days during the trip, fearing that such strain might injure him permanently.

The owners of the horses greeted him with a welcome when he returned their mounts, unhurt. He paid each of them a substantial amount for the service, although most of them protested his generous action.

On the afternoon of the eighteenth day after he had left Cynthiana, he rode into town, leading the famous racehorse. He stopped at Joe Bailey's, and had him accompany him to the sheriff's office.

A crowd gathered along the streets, following them, and applauding the man who had returned the great horse. They must know about it—how it was done, where, etc. But John and Bailey pushed on to the sheriff before explaining details.

The sheriff had learned of John's arrival and was standing on the steps, smiling.

"Well, if you hadn't come in two more days, I'd have been on your trail," the sheriff told him.

"Yeah, you'd have played the devil! You're too weak-kneed to follow a thief, much less an honest man. You let little things like the Ohio River keep you from doing your duty."

That brought a roar from the people, similar to those John had heard the day he had left on the chase.

When the commotion had subsided, the sheriff told John to come into his office and receive the necessary papers for his reward for capturing the criminal. The owner of the horse had put up the reward.

"I've already got my reward," John explained.

"Who paid you?" the sheriff asked.

"The thief."

"The—*who*? The thief paid you?"

John took off his coat and showed the bullet hole, then bent his head to show where the slug had cut a furrow, very light, but definite, above his right ear.

"Were you hit anywhere else?" the sheriff asked, excitedly.

"No. But it was the closest call of my life. I did not know that he was left-handed."

52

Then John exhibited his roll of currency, minus what he had given the owners of the animals he had ridden, and other expense money.

"This is my reward, sheriff," he said. "The thief paid his own reward."

"You've earned it," the sheriff said. "And for my part, you may keep it."

Chapter VII

Back to the Mountains

John Wright watched autumn come and go—a Bluegrass autumn. To him, September never did pass, but *faded* into October. Leaves began to drop upon the waning grass. The time of harvest had come; the time when John's heart was always filled with gladness. But not now.

During the pleasant months there had been a serious conflict raging within him. He yearned for the mountains as he had never yearned before. He longed for old rugged Pine Mountain, where he could hear the squirrels bark, chase the deer and the bear, attend corn shuckings, bean stringings, apple peelings, and the other social functions which marked this season of the year.

He wanted again to be a free man, to be one of his own people, where each did as he desired to do, unhampered by the rules of society, such as existed in the land of his wife, whom he loved with all his heart. There, he thought, he was looked upon with an eye of pity; he was, in their minds, an inferior subject, not equal in any sense with the refined people who inhabited that section. Consequently he was shorn of the right to exercise his personality, his initiative, to branch out into a life for himself.

Whether these things were real or imaginary mattered not at all. He was fully determined to return to his own land. He wished that his wife might go with him, but if she refused, he'd go alone.

These facts he explained to his wife.

"Wherever you go, I'll go," she told him in her gentle manner. "Wherever you stay, I'll stay."

"But if I can't stand your people, maybe you can't stand mine," he replied honestly.

"I *can*. I can stand them because I love *you*. I'm willing to bear anything to make your life happy, John. My own happiness depends upon yours."

John Wright felt like a great big boy who had just been licked by a small one. He felt humiliated. He turned away and left her. He must be alone now.

Once away from her sight he sat down to meditate. Never in life had he been outdone or let anyone else do something which he himself would not do. Now here was his wife—the weaker sex—willing to go anywhere, live or die, in order to be with *him*. No! he thought. He would not let her sacrifice her own happiness for his!

Arising quickly, he returned to her.

"We stay here!" he told her. "You don't love me any more than I love you. If you're willing to sacrifice your life for me, I'm willing to sacrifice mine, if necessary, for you."

The flash in his dark gray eyes told her that further conversation on the subject at that time was unnecessary, and it was dropped.

That was in early October. It passed slowly, its warm, invigorating days changed into cooler ones, then cold ones of December.

Meanwhile Martha, who knew that John was not happy, wished to make him so, and devised a scheme to overcome him. All along she had told him that she wanted to go to the mountains, but he thought it was only because *he* was homesick. However, her argument grew stronger and more convincing.

"John," she pleaded earnestly now, "I want to see the mountains, the big animals you say are there, the deep forests—everything. Some people tell me there are no bears and deer in the mountains. You know I believe you, but I do want to see for myself."

She had struck the explosive point. He had told her of killing the deer, and bear. Now, his word was being disputed.

"Well, we'll go see 'em. And we'll eat 'em, too," he told her.

Just before Christmas, about 1870, John and his Bluegrass wife started for the mountains. The trip was a treat for Martha. For the first time she saw the rugged hills grow into huge mountains and the meandering streams, the little log cabins and the mountain life.

On Christmas Day, they arrived at John's uncle's, Jesse Bates, on Millstone Creek, in Letcher County, under the shadow of Pine Mountain.

Immediately upon arrival, John and Bates went out and soon returned with a deer. This was the first one Martha had ever seen, dead or alive. It was skinned and prepared for the table. With wide eyes, Martha looked on as the animal was prepared. The meal from which the bread was made was ground by hand, by the rubbing together of two large cut stones; the coffee was bought in the green bean, roasted on the open fire, then placed in a tin can and ground by beating with the end of an axe handle or other blunt instrument.

A big fire crackled in the large, stone chimney, mended frequently by the addition of another log. Upon this fire the deer was roasted. Down on the hearth, where the live coals were raked, a large, round skillet or baking vessel, covered with a heavy lid, held a big pone of corn bread, being baked brown, its original flavor sustained by the lid.

The following day John and Martha traveled to his

father's, on the North Fork of Kentucky River, where they spent the winter.

In the spring he bought a small tract of land off the heirs of his grandfather Wright, which was a part of the old original Wright settlement.

[handwritten margin note: LAND purchase 1871 (spring)]

The long, lonely months that followed were a test of Martha's love for John. There were times when she almost despaired, but her love for the dashing mountain youth whom she had nursed back to health following the Cynthiana battle, was never to die. She soon learned the ways of the people, *his* people, and adapted herself to them. She learned that the mountain women were not spared the toil of the field, and, like the others, she took a hoe upon her shoulder when the housework was over and went to the field, where she worked until time to prepare dinner. Dinner over, dishes done, she returned and worked until time to begin supper and the housework for the night.

Meanwhile, John spent no idle moments. When the work of the little farm was up he was out trading and trafficking, following the footsteps of his father and grandfather. His early training, his exceptional natural ability, his war experiences, and his long travel with the world's greatest show, placed him head and shoulders above his fellow countrymen.

Consequently he at once became a leader. Rarely a question came up which John Wright could not answer. And so he was made a sort of information bureau to whom both old and young went for solutions to their problems.

His war record, running down outlaw bands in the mountains, and his successful battle with the criminal who stole the racehorse at Cynthiana, were not only known throughout the mountains, but had been heralded over many states.

Soon after his removal to the head of Boone's Fork, upon

his own land, he was made a deputy sheriff of Letcher County,

This position imposed untold hazards and hardships upon the men who filled it. Consequently but few would accept it.

Although the war, officially, was over, and all honest men had gone back to their regular pursuits of life, yet the mountains of Kentucky resounded with the rifle and revolver fire of the bushwhacker, the pillager, the highwaymen.

From time immemorial, in all countries and sections, there have been those who looked upon life as being created for them only and that they were entitled to the best the land afforded, without the necessity of doing their part of the work.

When the war began, this class of outlaws grasped hands and shouted for joy. Heretofore they had been held down by rules of the mountain civilization, but now there was to be no such thing. War, for them, suspended all laws of human conduct. It was a cloak under which they would operate.

They were without politics, religion, or character, yet they separated into groups, some claiming to be Confederates "home guards," and others of the same ilk called themselves Unionists, guarding the safety of the people. The mission of neither was to preserve the Union nor establish the Confederacy, but to prey upon the helpless women and children, and old people, to pillage and destroy, for the gratification of their own bellies and minds. The atrocious crimes they committed during the war would make Quantrill's guerrillas on the Kansas-Missouri border look anemic.

The closing of the war and the return of many of the true sons of the mountains did not stop the work of these bands, but only retarded their progress. The same groups which had been formed in the early months of the war held together, though their numbers had been greatly reduced by the accurate fire of the true sons of the Union and the Confederacy—for both had fought them from every angle known to them. Yet it was impossible for even both armies to annihilate them completely.

Now the fragments of these outlaw bands continued to prey upon the innocent and helpless at every opportunity. Mountain passes were watched and guarded and strangers who attempted to pass through were held up and robbed, and often murdered, if they resisted. Cribs and smoke-houses were broken into at night, the contents taken; chickens were stolen, cattle and horses driven off while families looked on helplessly.

But the most common of these depredations was the theft of horses. And the horse was the most highly prized animal in the mountains. And rightly so, for he was the only means of travel from countryside to town, from one valley or mountain to another, and it was by his power that the ground was broken up and tilled, his strength brought the timber from the forests to the mills, and the lumber to markets. The necessities of life were hauled from far places to the mountain homes, for consumption. Then, there is no wonder when a thief stole a horse and was trailed hundreds of miles, and often strung up to the first tree available.

Such were the conditions prevalent when John Wright was made a deputy sheriff on Boone and the Upper Elkhorn Valley, in Letcher County. This was in the early 1870s.

Many raids were made upon these outlaws in the years that followed. One of the first horse-thief cases to come to John Wright, as an officer, was brought by two Virginia officers. They were looking for one Dave Lee, who had stolen a horse from their state. They asked John and his father to go with them in search of the thief.

After feeding the Virginia lawmen supper, the four rode

Regardless of the many differences between the "Halls, Jones, Reynolds and Wrights" they all worked hard to support their families in the most honest and decent manner. Here we see rafting logs at the mouth of Beaver Creek in Floyd County, being prepared to go down Big Sandy River to Cattlettsburg, where a dollar per tree was the going price. At the time Cattlettsburg was the largest hardwood market in the world. (Photo from Henry P. Scalf collection 1910.)

into the moonlight, which was often darkened by flying clouds. It was autumn and cool, very pleasant. Sparks flew from the rocks as the iron horseshoes plunged against them. The men rode silently as the manner of both the hunter and the hunted, now and then stopping to listen and discuss the progress of their course.

The four stopped at the head of Millstone Creek, alighted and led their horses away from the road, where they were secured to bushes. They came back to a bend in the road and placed themselves in readiness for the possible passing of Dave Lee. They had stopped in the bushes, at the end of a field, through which the path ran. Here, they waited. Just beyond them was the gap which led to Beaver Creek and the lower Big Sandy Valley. Most all criminals from Virginia passed this way, and John Wright insisted that Dave Lee would do likewise.

Not many minutes had passed before the officers heard the clanking of horses' feet.

The four men crept close to the fence and peered down through the field, which was spotted by the flying clouds passing under the moon.

Two men rode abreast up through the field, busily engaged in conversation, until they came within a few feet of the officers. Then they alighted and pulled the saddles off their horses, laid them upon the ground and sat down by them, leaning their heads against them. Their horses began to pick greedily.

"I calls it a streak of luck, gettin' through the Gap with *them* hawsees," one said.

"Yeah. And I'm obliged to think it's only kindness of Providence we ain't met John Wright," the other drawled lazily. "That depity don't sleep nor eat. He'd better never cross my path."

"Don't worry. He ain't as bad as he's said to be."

"Course not. He knows who to tackle."

The last speaker stretched out his legs and expressed

61

his relief in a long groan. The other eyed the two sweat-drenched horses picking near him.

Meanwhile, John Wright and his father had mounted the rail fence within a few feet of the resting men. John motioned with his hand for the two Virginia officers to follow him and his father, but they had lagged behind.

Thus far the presence of the officers was unknown to the thieves, who lounged upon the drying grass. John had a warrant for each of them and knew them by their voices. Neither was Dave Lee, for whom they had come to search, but these were bigger prizes than Lee.

"Hands up, fellers!" John Wright demanded as he and his father sprang from the top of the fence.

The thieves jumped to their feet, pulling their guns. Blazes shot from the muzzles of revolvers and the valley echoed with the roars. John's first shot disabled one of the men, his second one brought him to the ground before he could fire a shot. Meanwhile the other fired twice at John but then the latter's gun was turned on him. The thief had backed away and a dark cloud came over the moon at that second. This, together with the fire of the guns, somewhat blinded John until he could not well make out the form of the other man. However he fired the three remaining cartridges in his gun, taking the best aim possible, then started running after the man.

The fleeing thief ran for a hundred yards while John gained on him every step. Finally the man came to a high bank. It was either jump or fight. He jumped over the bank just as John was reaching to collar him.

John looked down over the bank and decided he did not want such a jump. Yet, he must not let the criminal escape. And so, reaching down, he picked up a large stone and threw it, breaking the man's shoulder.

"Don't! You've killed me now!" the man begged pitifully.

John took his prisoner back to the scene of the shooting,

62

wondering what had happened to his father, who was as brave a man as ever lived. But his father's foot had slipped when he had started to spring from the fence and he fell, throwing his gun away and landing in some thick brush. When he got out one of the thieves was lying on the ground, groaning, and the other was fleeing from John.

The Virginia officers had taken refuge behind tall timbers nearby.

"Come on, fellers," John called. "It's all over now."

The Virginia officers climbed over the fence and walked up.

"Did you men think this was a funeral?" John asked them. "You were so quiet, you must have."

Groans from the wounded man relieved the officers from answering the embarrassing question.

An examination was made, by lighting matches. One shot had entered the left shoulder, the other had grazed the right temple. Neither was serious.

John, now bent on capturing Dave Lee, left the prisoners in the custody of his father and the two Virginia officers, advising them to take the prisoners to a neighbor's, down the creek, keep them there until he returned.

An hour later John hitched his horse within a hundred yards of the barn of one of his close friends and also a close relative, whom he had suspected of harboring horse thieves as they passed through with their loot. He approached silently towards the log barn, listening for the sound of horses, chewing on the remains of their feed— cobs, pieces of cornstalks, etc., which they never eat first. He found a strange horse in one stall, the kind which his two officer friends had described as the one stolen from their neighbor.

A few minutes later he knocked on the door of his relative.

"Who *air* you?" a familiar voice sounded.

"John Wright. Open up!"

"What do you want, John?"

"I want Dave Lee, and the stolen horse in your barn."

"I ain't seen Dave Lee tonight."

"Open this door or I'll shoot it down. I've warned you before. No more warnings. This is it."

There was a shuffling of feet.

Holding his revolver ready, John stood by the side of the door.

"Light a torch before opening the door," he demanded.

A pine torch was lighted and the door opened.

"Get out and put your clothes on, Lee," John said, still standing beside the door. "And come out, hands up."

Without hesitation, Lee crawled out of bed, jerked on his clothes and came out, hands up high.

With a "last warning" to his friend-relative, he and Lee started to join John's father, the two officers who had come for Lee, and the two prisoners.

The Virginia officers, amazed at John Wright's ability as an officer, promised to send him "much business" from the Old Dominion.

Chapter VIII

John Wright Moves to Elkhorn Valley

While John Wright was trailing criminals, farming, trading and trafficking in everything in which he could make a dollar, he was not asleep to the possibilities which lay around him. He now owned land on the headwaters of Boone Fork, valuable land, heavily timbered, and possessing a part of that vast deposit of coal which later was to be heralded across the entire world.

But his mind drew him across the mountain to the headwaters of Elkhorn Creek, a tributary of Big Sandy River. In Pound Gap and from Raven's Rock, just east of the gap, he had viewed many times the vast extent of wealth lying beneath him. Stretching to the north were low-lying hills and high mountains, covered with oak, poplar, walnut, pine, and under those hills, he knew were inexhaustible seams of coal, whose value he made no attempt to estimate. Some day, he thought, that coal would roll out of Big Sandy, from the Elkhorn side, and down the Kentucky River, from the western section. Would it come in his lifetime? he wondered.

"Little Elkhorn" extended back to its source under Pound Gap, and against the headwaters of the North Fork of Kentucky River, and, on the south, against the head of Boone Fork. The forks of the stream were directly

65

beneath Raven Rock. On his left was "Goodwater" branch, so called because of the ever-running spring of pure, clear water, always cold.

John Wright stood or sat on Raven Rock many times, enhanced by the threading of the great fingers of nature as the headwaters of the various branches of the Kentucky River reached back, interlapping with the head streams of Elkhorn, the two Beaver Creeks, Shelby Creek —down which General Isaac Shelby had marched his troops, later to become Kentucky's first governor. All this country was yet a vast wilderness, not far removed from the state in which Daniel Boone had found it several decades ago. It was still filled with an abundance of wild game, and in its clear, pure streams were fish of the finest species. Laurel and rhododendron covered the ground so thick that in places one had to cut his way through it. Kentucky River, running westward or north-westward, was like a great serpent, winding and turning, and wooded down to its waters.

The industrious, enterprising mountain sleuth had viewed these scenes with a view to the future, saving every dollar possible, with which he would purchase some of these lands. Meanwhile, his Bluegrass wife, Martha, now affectionately called "Mattie," worked daily, saved, looking eagerly to the time when complete happiness and economic comfort might come to her home.

The time *did* come when John Wright was able to purchase land around the forks of Elkhorn. A simple log cabin home was erected at the mouth of Goodwater Branch, at the intersection of three roads. The road to Pikeville, county seat of Pike County, and the Big Sandy Valley, ran east, down the valley; the Pound Gap road, now U.S. 23, turned south, climbing Pine Mountain; the third road traversed the headwaters of main Elkhorn, crossing the low pass into the Potter's Fork of the North Fork of Kentucky River.

66

Cutting through Shelby Gap in Pike County to make way for the Shelby Valley and Elkhorn Railroad, a short stretch of track that eventually connected Shelby Creek with Elkhorn City and Jenkins, near the home of "Devil" John Wright.

The wares and merchandise sold in Whitesburg and Letcher County, were hauled either from Abingdon, Virginia, or from Pikeville, Kentucky. From the latter point, only whenever there was sufficient water in Big Sandy to allow boats to ply to that point. Consequently the home of John Wright soon became a haven for the wagoners, horseback riders, and even pedestrians. No one was ever turned from the Wright door. If John Wright had objected to accommodating a hungry, weary man, his wife, Mattie, would not have allowed him his pleasure. But in this, the two agreed heartily. If the guest had no money, the service was the same as if he had had it, and the fare to those who could pay, was nominal, thirty-five cents for supper, lodging, and breakfast for a man and his two horses.

About this time, and before, there came into the mountains "furriners," men looking over the possibilities that might lie there. As a result, large tracts of land were surveyed and grants secured on them at *five cents per acre.* One of these prospectors was W. D. Jones, who represented a firm in Philadelphia. John Wright formed acquaintance with Jones, in Whitesburg, and they became warm friends. Jones came and went, and bought many tracts of land, through the help of John Wright, who knew everybody and knew how to approach them.

Then ushered in the memorable eighties.

Career Change

It was in the early eighties that John Wright switched from the enforcement side of the law to the judicial. He was elected magistrate. Upon taking office, he said to the people:

"Nobody wins in law. The winner loses, and the loser loses more. Don't law!"

Tradition tells us that whenever he found grievances based on prejudice or a rash act in anger, he called both parties together and went over the matter slowly, patiently, and in many cases had them to agree to drop their differences.

In those days there was little road building going on. Now and then a wagon trail would be extended a mile or two. But most repairs were done by the citizens, each working six days a year, which the law required.

It was while serving as magistrate that John Wright acquired the title, "The Tall Sycamore of the Elkhorn." One of his duties as magistrate was to help run the boundaries, creating the new county of Knott.

The judicial side of the law did not appeal to John Wright as had the enforcement. He declined another term.

In September 1883, the peaceful little Elkhorn Valley was aroused by the coming of strangers, "furriners," but different ones from W. D. Jones and his crew of a few years ago.

These men were asked to tell their business, as all strangers must do in those times. No man was safe to go anywhere in these mountains without explaining his mission. If he had a legitimate business, and it did not infringe upon what the mountaineer considered his freedom or privilege, he was welcomed. But should he be, for instance, a revenue officer, prying into their still locations or places of sale of mountain dew, he was sticking his neck out, and how!

But the party who came to the head of Elkhorn in the fall of 1883 were glad to tell their mission there. It was prospectors, headed by the eminent engineer, Richard M. Broas, who had been a Federal captain in the Civil War. Broas and his engineers had come to look over the Elkhorn coal seams, of which he had heard much.

During the War Between the States, observing soldiers of the East, for the most part Federal officers, had seen in their hurried march through the region outcroppings of the now famous "Elkhorn" coal. Notes were made and

69

Wagon entering coal camp at Jenkins during early days. John Wright was a leader in coal development, and was one of the planners of the building of Jenkins.

carried until the close of the war, then taken to New York, when the officers returned home. Whether Richard M. Broas ever came through the area is doubtful. But he was one of the great engineers of the country, and a specialist in minerals, always searching for the choicest the earth afforded. He searched over the West for gold and silver.

Captain Broas had prospected from Louisa, at the confluence of the Levisa and Tug Forks of Big Sandy River, southward, locating the great "Miller's Creek Block" coal at Van Lear, in Johnson County, before coming to Ashcamp, to find the quality of coal there of excellent coking grade, but, being in the Cumberland Mountain, limited in extent. Then he had pushed on up romantic Elkhorn Valley to its headwaters, making camp within a few hundred yards of John Wright's home, or "Mattie's House," at the mouth of Goodwater Branch, where the beautiful *Home Site* Jenkins Lake is now located, on U.S. Route 23.

Having heard of so many gruesome tales of the mountains, the newcomers were naturally skeptical *of* the rough-clad, beardy mountaineers who visited them, asking questions in a manner which prompted quick answers from them.

But John Wright soon allayed the fears of both the engineers and his own people, explaining to both the meaning of the other. The party under Broas saw in Wright, not the mountain outlaw which they had been taught to believe of most mountain men, but the glowing warmth of a friend in need. John was persuaded to guard the group during the first few nights, despite his protests that no guard was needed; that, since their mission there was for the good of the people, they would be warm and protective friends, the same as himself.

Included in Captain Broas's party of surveyors, prospectors, and title investigators was the late prominent Judge John F. Hager, of Ashland, Kentucky. Soon Professor Crandall, of the Kentucky Geological Survey joined them and insisted that a specimen of the coal be blocked out, packed and shipped to Louisville for the Southern Exposition to be held the following month.

To their surprise, John Wright showed the party coal eight feet high, clean of all dirt, right on his own land. The party went to work and blocked out a piece of the black diamond, two feet in diameter and the full height of eight feet. John Wright made a sled, large and strong, and hitched a string of oxen to it, and hauled the piece of coal to Pikeville, forty miles. From there it was shipped by pushboat to Ashland, 120 miles, and from there by train to Louisville for the exposition.

Captain Broas and his men continued the work, opening entries, digging out coal and making tests, surveying, prospecting. Gossip filled the countryside. Some natives

71

wore eager faces, in hope that soon their country might be opened to the world, yet others, who had never seen the outside of the mountains, and in addition, had harbored a prejudice and suspicion against anyone not their own, detested the thought of "furriners" coming into their midst.

But in the height of this work, there came a sad disappointment to Captain Broas and his loyal party. Nathaniel Stone Sympkins, one of the owners of the Calumet Heccla Copper Company, of Cape Cod, Massachusetts, Broas's main financial backer, died and the work was ordered suspended indefinitely.

Chapter IX

John Wright's Greatest Manhunt

John Wright and his loyal wife, Martha, now called "Mattie," were planting a new ground in corn on a fine spring morning, after moving into their new home on upper Elkhorn, when they had two guests from West Virginia. The men were officers. The fact that the newcomers carried rifles and revolvers meant nothing to John Wright. Most men in the mountains did that, especially those traveling around. He thought that they were hunting for work, and he needed help.

"I'll pay you men fifty cents a day and board," he told them seriously.

One of the officers scowled, the other laughed.

"We want to hire *you*," the amiable one replied.

John eyed them suspiciously.

"Who do you want killed?" he asked.

"Well," the officer said, sizing Wright up, "we don't know. But the law wants somebody killed or brought to jail. In the first place, we don't know who it is, and if we did—" He paused as a hound began barking violently just outside the field.

"What's the dog barking at?" the scowling officer asked.

"Oh, a squirrel. He trees forty a day."

73

The officer dismounted, took his rifle and hurried toward the dog.

"I'm too busy to go man-hunting," John Wright told him. He waved over the freshly cleared new ground, where his wife was digging holes with a heavy hoe and dropping a few grains of corn into each, then covering the grains with black, fertile soil.

"I see," the officer said, unaffected. "But there are others who can do this work. Not everyone can catch criminals. We've heard of your work and were sent here to see you about taking on the case. Bring this man in and get five hundred."

"Couldn't *you* use five hundred?" John replied.

"*Could* I? You bet, and that's why I've spent months trying to find the man who burned old man Makin's store, after breaking in his skull. We can't get even a clue. If you—"

The crack of a rifle brought their eyes around in time to see a squirrel fall from a tree outside the fence.

"My partner would rather hunt game than men," the officer said, grinning. "But getting back—"

"Probably you've been thinking more about the five hundred than of catching your man," John interrupted goodnaturedly.

"What do you mean?" the officer asked, his eyes narrowing slightly.

"The love of money, you know," John explained. "It can blind you to the facts in your case."

"Isn't that why *you* catch them?"

"Part of the reason. But I love the game, even if there wasn't a dollar in it. I feel that I owe my services to my fellowmen."

"Then come and find the man who killed Makin," the West Virginian urged.

"I can't do it now," John said, his eyes glancing at his wife, who had never slowed her pace, planting corn. "But tell me all you know about it and I'll think it over while you men try to find the killer." John had already heard vaguely about the burning of the store, the finding of the owner's burned body. But that was all.

"The store was burned about three o'clock in the morning," the officer explained. "Mr. Makin slept in the back of the store. He kept money with him most of the time, going to the bank only once a week. He paid most of his bills by cash. He had no iron safe, but did have an old trunk for the purpose."

"Did he have any known enemies?" John inquired.

"None at all. A fine man that everybody liked."

"Who was his *best* friend?"

"Oh—well, everybody. Nobody dis—."

"But *somebody* was, apparently, his best friend," John insisted.

"Well—," he meditated a few seconds. "Why, Jack Lawson, Makin's cousin," he explained.

"Where's Jack Lawson now?" John asked.

"I don't know," he replied. "I saw him every day until —oh, on second thought, I haven't seen him since last fall. Confound it, how did I fail to miss him?"

The scowling officer returned, carrying a squirrel, a large hound at his feet.

"What kind of feller was Jack Lawson?" John Wright wanted to know.

"Pretty nice young man—well, not an old man—except that he wouldn't work. And he gambled a lot and drunk some, but he was goodhearted—"

"Goodhearted with his own property or that of others?" John Wright interrupted again.

"Well, come to think of it, he never had of his own, to speak of."

"Where was Lawson the night of the fire?"

"By golly! I'd never thought of it, but I saw the store burning. Gus Ray and I had been hunting, and as we came

75

in sight we saw the big light and rushed on. As we passed Lawson's house, which was close, I saw Jack dart in at the back door."

"Didn't Lawson come to the burning store after that?"

"Yes, after the neighbors had gathered around, I saw him there, and heard him asking questions, and wiping his eyes, as if crying over the death of his cousin."

"And you don't know where Lawson has gone?" John asked.

"No, I don't. Nor have I heard his name spoken since he left."

"Find this man Lawson and collect the five hundred," John told the officers. "He's your man."

The two officers exchanged puzzled glances, then looked pleadingly at John Wright.

"If you don't find him, come back when my corn's planted, and I'll try to help you," he promised them.

John Wright's corn had been planted and hoed the first time before the West Virginian returned. This time, it was only the one who had given John Wright the information concerning the murder of the Makin store owner. The two men had exhausted all their strategy and patience, but had gotten no trace of Jack Lawson's whereabouts. Lawson's parents explained that he had gone to the West, where he had always wanted to live.

Jack Lawson's parents had a large farm and employed help frequently now, since the son had left.

Wright accompanied the officer to West Virginia, separating before arriving at the latter's home.

"Take my horse and keep him," John Wright told the officer. "And don't forget to feed him! I'm going to hire to the old man Lawson—at any wages he wants to pay."

"What do you want me to do?" the officer asked.

"Stay here and let nobody know that you know me. Tell

'em my horse is one you've traded for. When I get things ready, I'll let you know."

The Lawsons lived in a large, two-story log house which had been weatherboarded on the outside and ceiled on the inside—a very comfortable home in winter or summer. A large chimney, of native stone, adorned each end. The elder Lawson was sixty-odd years old and had two beautiful daughters, spinsters. They lived three miles from the post office and stores and on each Saturday it was John's duty to take one or both of them in the two-seated hack and bring back groceries for the next week, and bring the mail.

Contrary to the wish of the girls, he would accompany them into the post office and slyly scan the mail they got, or sent out. As a pretence he would call for mail for his assumed name—Bill Gose, but never received any.

The first two Saturdays he saw no mail going or coming which looked suspicious.

At the Lawson home he quizzed the girls about their "sweetheart" mail, hoping to draw something out of them. Every letter either of them received, he would want to see it, pretending to be jealous. But the girls seemed to sense something wrong and kept all their mail hidden from him.

John refrained from asking the elderly Lawson any question, fearing that he might arouse suspicion. He told Lawson that he, himself, was wanted in another state for a minor offense and must ask that he be paid each week, so that if he had to leave in a hurry there would be nothing to delay him.

John Wright knew that the family was corresponding with the son. He must find out where Jack Lawson was!

And so in his upstairs room, directly over the one in which the two girls lived, he conceived a plan. Tomorrow the girls would be washing down at the creek, by the big hole of water. They would be absent from the room for some hours. The elderly Mrs. Lawson would sit out under the weeping willow and knit and would not be concerned about anything else.

The next morning when things worked around as he had hoped, he took an auger from the smokehouse, where the tools were kept, and bored a hole through the floor of his room, directly above the table in the girls' room, upon which they did their writing. He then made a round peg with which he stopped the hole, polishing it until it looked just like the floor. The shavings which dropped down into the girls' room were swept up and stuck in his pocket until he could get a chance to burn them. He watched every letter either of the girls received or wrote, and could read every word of it.

A week passed before his opportunity came.

The tall, beautiful girl sat down by the table and took a ruled tablet from a drawer, and with a pencil began to write:

Dearest Uncle:
This leaves us all well. Hope you are all right.

She paused, sticking the end of the pencil in her mouth and running it back and forth across her teeth. Then she resumed:

This is an awful life, knowing that Jack will some day be caught. Dad's worrying himself to death.
Keep him from coming home and be sure that no officers find him.

She paused again, as if she had intended to close the letter, but suddenly she began to write:

Say, Uncle, there is the cutest fellow here. He says he's single and—well, he says he's done something against the law, somewhere, but—anyway, he's CUTE!

John Wright's heart pounded for two reasons—the girl, and the fact that until now, he had learned nothing as to Jack Lawson's whereabouts. He kept his eye glued on the

78

pencil. At last, the girl took an envelope and began to address it:

Mr. Early Brayley,
Slippery, W. Va.

John Wright replaced the peg in the hole and prepared to leave the Lawson home.

Deputy Marvin rose quickly when John Wright rapped on his door.

"Get ready to follow me," John ordered the officer. "Never mind asking about clews. Your job will be to catch me. I've stolen a horse and am headed for Slipperey, West Virginia. Do plenty of pretending, but be sure you don't overtake me."

"Hey, Mr. Wright—wait! Did you say, *Slipperey*?"

"I said, Slipperey. Why?"

"For the Lord's sake, man! That's a hundred miles from here, in the toughest part of the state. You couldn't ride a jackass into that wilderness."

"If Jack Lawson got there, we can, can't we?"

"Durned if I don't dread that trip, Mr. Wright. But I'm with you, since I got you into this mess," Marvin promised.

Within thirty minutes John Wright was riding toward one of the roughest sections in the West Virginia mountains. Marvin was to follow a few hours later, but was to ask no questions until he came to a designated spot, close to Jack Lawson's location.

On the afternoon of the third day Wright learned where old Brayley lived—up a creek, off the main road. He took the trail through the woodland and let his horse go slow until he emerged into the clearing in which the house stood. Then he spurred up the horse and galloped on to the house, alighted hurriedly and dashed up to the doorway, where an elderly man stood, eyeing him suspiciously.

"Say, Uncle," Wright panted, as if out of breath, "I'm

79

in trouble. The law's after me. Will you keep my horse hid somewhere and let me hide around here for a few days?"

Brayley frowned as he observed the tall young man, a pistol on each hip; noting his smiling gray eyes.

"Well, I reckon, son," he said slowly. "I hate to turn people down that need help."

John Wright followed the elderly man up the creek a short distance to a large, log barn, with a shed built all around it.

"Now, son, make yourself to home," Brayley told him, warming up in tone. "I'll go back and if them officers come and 'sist on searching the barn I'll accidentally tap the dinner bell, sorter light, you know. And if you hear it, take that path," indicating a bridle path leading out into the forest. "It'll lead you plumb out'n reach."

"And if the lawmen come and go back, I'll let you know."

John Wright watched the elderly man waddle back towards his home, his fat hands swinging out from his sides, as if with an effort.

Wright climbed up into the loft of the big barn and lay down in the soft hay. Soon he fell asleep. He had lost nights of sleep reaching here.

At twilight, Deputy Marvin and a neighbor who had come with him, rode up to the gate and called.

Brayley walked slowly to meet them.

"We're looking for a tall, dark man, young, with sharp gray eyes, riding a bay horse. Have you seen anyone of this description, Uncle?" Marvin asked.

"No, sir, mister, nobody of that kind has passed here." Brayley answered.

Marvin turned to his partner.

"I'd have sworn to the track, wouldn't you, Joe?"

The other was silent, as if meditating, for a moment. Then he spoke.

80

"Well, Mr. Marvin, a feller could be mistaken. I've been before. I wouldn't swear to the track. It looked like the stolen mare's track, but—" He stopped.

"Now, I tell you, boys," Brayley explained, "hawss' tracks are purty much alike. I guess it was my nag's tracks you seen."

"Would you mind let us see your horse?" Marvin asked.

"There's no use pestering the man," Marvin's partner protested. "That horse thief's gone the other way. I told you that, way back, and if we're to catch him, we'd better be hitting that way."

"Oh, well, just as you say, Joe." Then Marvin turned to Brayley, saying,

"We may be back this way. Keep your eyes open for this thief we're after, will you?"

"I sure will, son. And I'll rope him myself if he comes around. How I hate horse thieves."

Smart officers! Brayley thought, as he hurried to the barn with the good news.

A few minutes later, Brayley, Wright, and a small elderly woman, sat down to steaming hot coffee, streaked bacon, eggs, corn pone and rich milk and butter. The woman's face showed signs of many troubles, by the deep furrows across it.

Brayley asked his guest many and varied questions, which John Wright answered, all to his host's apparent satisfaction.

Bedtime came, as it always does with the mountain farmer, unless he has something "on" for the night. The one-story log house had two rooms besides a kitchen, boxed off on one side, of rough boards.

"You kin sleep in the lower room, son," Brayley told John Wright. He promptly accepted and retired.

There was no door between the two rooms, and the partition was a log wall. Whenever one wished to go from one room to the other, he had to go out the door of his apartment and into the door of the other one, crossing the front porch.

As was his custom, Wright looked the wall over carefully before retiring. Fortunately he found where part of one of the oaken boards, used for stopping the cracks between the logs, had cupped far enough from the wall to allow him to listen to what was said on the other side, in the adjoining room. Unfortunately for him, the old people soon fell asleep without revealing anything which he wished to know. They wondered about him, where he was from, what he had done, etc.

Next morning, Wright was awakened by a violent knocking on his door. He had barred the door before retiring.

"Hey, young man!" It was Brayley's voice.

"What is it?" Wright asked, uneasily.

"Snake out of there! Breakfast's ready, son!"

At the breakfast table, Wright stretched himself, yawned, and complained about not sleeping last night.

"What was the trouble?" Brayley asked. "The bed hard?" The haggard old lady looked steadfastly to get his answer.

"Oh, no," Wright hastened to explain. "The bed was fine, better than I'm used to. You see, I'm always in a dread. The law's after me every way I look. No matter where I go, the law's there, and if I stay here, the law's here, so can a feller sleep?"

The two old ones looked pityingly, their faces sad.

"But I wouldn't grieve, son," Brayley soothed. "What've you don agin the law?"

"Plenty. Killed two men—"

"Ooh! *Murdered* 'em?" This from the old woman.

"I don't call it murder," Wright said calmly. "They were both on me and I had to outshoot 'em or die."

"I don't call it murder," declared Brayley. "But what can the law do with you, if it was self-defense?"

"You see," Wright explained, "all the witnesses are for the other side. None for me."

"Uh huh. I see the point now," said Brayley.

Then to his wife, he said,

"Ma, we'll have to help the young man."

"I reckon so," she grunted, barely audibly.

Breakfast over, Wright followed Brayley to the barn and helped do the chores.

It was a late June morning. Dew-drenched timber glistened under the rising sun; wild flowers, filled with dew, opened and spread out under the warm rays, and birds flitted about in the forest nearby, singing a song of happiness which neither Brayley nor Wright could fully appreciate.

From place to place during the day, John Wright followed the fat old man, hoping that, in some way, his host might reveal the lair of Jack Lawson. Now and then, Wright would tell of another offense, for which he had evaded the law. But Brayley remained silent on the matter which Wright wished to learn.

After lunch, Wright asked Brayley for the shotgun, which he had seen hanging over the door of the old people's room.

"I like to kill squirrels, and I like to eat 'em," Wright said, truthfully.

"Yes, son, take the gun and kill us a nice mess of squirrels. I'm getting too old to hunt, but how I used to kill 'em!"

Wright followed the bridle path which Brayley had shown him the day before. He watched closely for bypaths, but found where not more than one track had left the path at any single place.

On top of the ridge above the Brayley home, he studied the "lay of the land." Beneath him on the other side of the ridge, was a deep, dark ravine which seemed to have no end. It looked impossible for man to penetrate the thick laurel, rhododendron, grapevines, and other obstructions. Here the trail turned off a diagonal course, evading the jungle.

Upon close examination Wright found little openings through which, it appeared, persons had gone. Probably it was hunters after deer or bear. And then—well, Jack Lawson might be hiding somewhere in that vast jungle.

When the sun dropped behind a tall mountain, casting deep shadows upon him, he was still studying the small openings leading into—he knew not what.

One thing he would find out—soon. The right shoe of the track which had gone into so many different openings in the forest had a split in the sole, making a kind of triangle in the middle of the track. This he had seen in several places where the soft loam had shown the track plainly.

As he went back in, he noticed the tracks around the barn in the soft places and was happy to find so many of them with the identical marks of the right shoe in the forest.

It had been no trouble to kill as many squirrels as he cared to bring in, since they barked all around him. And so when he threw down half a dozen on the floor, the fat Mr. Brayley wrinkled in a smile.

"I suppose you wish you were young again, so you could climb the mountains," Wright said, teasingly.

The old man's blue eyes flashed with something which Wright took for a moment, as detection of the motive for asking the question. But that look disappeared quickly.

"But bet I do, son," Brayley answered. "But that can't never be agin."

At the supper table, Wright saw a clean meal sack, about half full of something, tied securely and standing against the kitchen wall, near the stove.

That night he failed to hear anything said between the old folks that would help him, but he felt sure that the sack in the kitchen contained food, and he was determined to watch its destination, come what might.

But he reasoned that the old man could hardly make that trip in the night, carrying a load and a torch, as he would have to do. And the tracks, which were surely the old man's, dispersed any theory that anyone else was carrying food to the fugitive. Consequently, after midnight, when he knew by their heavy breathing, that the old couple were asleep, he fell asleep.

The next morning Wright was detailed by Brayley to go up the creek half a mile, to a field, to see whether some cattle had torn down his fence and gotten into the field. They had been doing this, the elderly fat man explained, and he feared that they might again.

"And take the gun along," Brayley suggested, "so you can kill us another mess of squirrels."

A dense fog hung low and the weeds and bushes were drenched with dew. Wright had not gone far before his feet and legs were soaked.

As soon as John Wright entered the woodland above the house, he turned back towards the path over which he had gone the previous day. Within a few minutes, he topped the ridge, using all precaution, thinking that Jack Lawson, who was surely hiding in the jungle, might come to the ridge to meet Brayley. The fog was so thick that it seemed it could be cut with a butter knife, making it easy for a woodsman to steal through forest unseen and unheard.

Thirty minutes later he heard someone coming up the path, panting and blowing. A few more minutes and old Brayley, hat in hand, and meal sack across his shoulder, emerged into view. Every few steps he would stop and fan his face with his hat and wipe the perspiration with the sleeve of his shirt.

Within a few feet of Wright, he sat down upon a log. He wiped and fanned simultaneously.

Wright stepped out from behind a tree and walked towards him.

"Hey—what's *your* business here?" Brayley demanded, eyes wide with apparent fright.

"Listen, Uncle," Wright said calmly, and sat down beside the old man. "I'm getting scared around here, staying out in the open, like I've been doing. I saw this wilderness yesterday and I'm satisfied there must be good hiding places—out that way." He pointed toward the canyon, into which he had seen the old man's tracks proceeding."

Brayley's eyes held Wright's for a moment, apparently undecided on his reaction.

"And I hunted back this way this morning, to look it over again. But how did I know I was to meet *you* here?"

"Well, I—er—"

"Listen, Uncle, I've got some money, and I'm willing to pay you to help me. You take me right now and show me somewhere to stay, and keep my horse till I take a notion to leave this part of the country. You'll have to bring me something to eat now and then." He glanced at the sack, then back at Brayley's eyes, which were almost closed as he was apparently, trying to reach a decision. Presently the old man straightened up and looked Wright squarely in the eyes—again, but this time with resolution.

"Come on!" he said, with enthusiasm. "I'll take you where you'll be safe and have a pardner, too. Carry that sack of grub."

"Grub?" Wright said, as if he had not noticed the sack.

"Yes, grub, bread, sow belly, beans, an' coffee. Enough to do you a week."

For a mile, they fought their way through the jungle, sometimes crawling on hands and knees, finally reaching a mountain of rock, stretching up and down the canyon.

It appeared at first to Wright that there was nothing

but a solid wall of rock before them. Then, the mountain sleuth's eyes caught the lay of it all. He saw tracks leading to a small slit in the cliff. And this crevice was formed, running up and down the mountain, in the same direction as the cliff, so that its detection was hard to detect for one not versed in the ways of the mountains.

Instinctively Wright's eyes scanned every nook and corner, crevice, or opening, suddenly his keen eyes catching the muzzle of a high-power rifle protruding from a small crack, and pointing directly at him. Wright paused and his hand shot to a pistol on his side. But Brayley, seeing the movements, yelled,

"It's all right, Jack!" He waved his chubby hand as he spoke, signaling the other to put down his gun.

Wright walked faster than Brayley up the steep climb to the entrance. He stood at the mouth of the cave, facing as desperate looking character as he had ever met. A well built man, of a combination of red and light complexion, his eyes half closed, his left foot forward and his rifle nearly to his shoulder. Sphinx-like, he stood, eyeing the intruder at the mouth of the entrance. For seconds the caveman stood, never a tremor in his posture.

Meanwhile, Wright had kept his hand upon his revolver butt before reaching his position. Wright knew this man now; knew what he had done—killed a cousin, then burned his store, taking all the cash he could find. This man, he knew, would take no chances. This was Jack Lawson!

During the few seconds, which appeared an age, the desperateness, the courage of each was instilled into the other. Wright felt that he had the gravest problem before him that he had ever confronted before.

Finally, old Brayley reached the entrance. But the caveman broke the silence.

"What'n hell's *your* business here?" he demanded.

"The same's yours, old top," Wright answered, "beating the law."

"Jack, put down your gun," Brayley said. "I've fetched you a pardner. He's got you beat a whole passel. He's killed a dozen men."

"You old fool!" Lawson growled harshly. "How do you know how many men he's killed!'

"Because the officers trailed him to my house," Brayley explained. "I've been hidin' him three days."

At these words, Lawson relaxed his gun hold and stood it by the side of the cliff. His eyes still held fast on the newcomer.

"What's your name, and where you from?" Lawson asked shortly.

"To you, I'm Mell Dix, but that ain't my name, and I come from London, England, but that ain't my home."

Lawson's brows wrinkled into a frown.

"If you're on the square, why can't you tell your name?" Lawson insisted.

"In the first place, I ain't on the square. If I was, I wouldn't come into this devil's backyard. And neither would you. Why put on the dog, partner? Be human, if you are, like me, a criminal, cheating the law."

"Well, if neither of us is on the square, why would either of us care to tell his name to the other?" Lawson persisted.

"A very good reason. Suppose one of us was to be caught and the other left, and it should be left up to the one taken in to tell where the other one was or be hung? Well, I'd tell, and so would you. That's why you don't get *my* name."

Lawson seemed to be satisfied that Wright was actually "on the square," a criminal. Apparently the mistrust and apprehension disappeared.

"Well, you can call me Jack, but that ain't my name, Mr. Dix," Lawson said with a bit of warmth now.

"Call me Mell," Wright told him.

Brayley and Wright sat at the mouth of the entrance

88

until Jack Lawson went into the cave and emptied the sack and returned. Then Brayley proceeded on his rough journey back through the wilderness.

"Go on in," Lawson invited his uninvited guest. "We'll get a bite to eat."

For a hundred feet, Wright led the way, Lawson directing, down a narrow, dark cave until he came to where it grew too small for further passage.

"Go in at the window," Lawson explained.

By now, Wright's eyesight had become accustomed to the inside and he could discern a small ledge on the side of the rock, and above it, an opening. Without hesitation, he climbed upon the ledge, stripped his guns from his sides and squeezed through, finding on the other side a large stone room, with an opening on the side.

He proceeded to this opening and looked out over the veritable jungle hundreds of feet below. The cave was absolutely inaccessible, save by the way they had come. It seemed that nature had placed the "window" in the side of the cavern to give light and air to those who might occupy it.

"Snug home you've got here, Jack," Wright complimented.

"You may think so now, but stay here awhile and you'll tell a different tale." Lawson was busying himself mending the little fire, around which were various vessels for cooking and eating.

"Skin them squirrels and we'll cook," Lawson said.

"Bet your boots I will," Wright replied, and stopped his observing of the surroundings and cleaned the two squirrels which Jack said he had killed early that morning near the cave entrance.

Soon there was a pone of bread baking on the coals. Bacon was frying, squirrels cooking, while on the other end of the fire, coffee was boiling, casting its delicious flavor over the stone room.

"Humph—home life!" Wright exclaimed. "You know I've been hounded from place to place so long, and never had a nice place like this to stay in—I really feel at home."

Jack Lawson laughed loudly.

"Home! It's no home for me—it's *hell*," he declared.

The two ate dinner, Wright eating greedily, for he could always eat more in the open on occasions like this than at home.

Meanwhile, there was never a moment when there were not wary glances from one to the other. Lawson carried a bright revolver on his left hip, and his hand movements told John Wright that he was dealing with a gunman, whether known or not. Wright could still detect suspicion in Lawson's eyes, his movements.

Lawson was a highly prized criminal in Wright's eyes. This caveman had eluded all detectives who had been on his trail. In fact, they had failed to find his trail! Wright felt somewhat self-important now, because he honestly believed that Lawson would have escaped suspicion if he, Wright, had not explained all of it to the West Virginia officers, who had come to him for assistance. Then, after sufficient evidence had leaked out to put them onto his trail, they had failed to find him.

Therefore he was determined to take him back—alive —regardless of the time it might take him. There had been times during the day when he could have arrested him or killed him. But knowing character as he did, he was convinced that the murderer would have died in his tracks, rather than be taken back to face a trial for the brutal murder of his uncle—for money. And he did not want to kill him. That would not sound as good in the ears of the world, besides, he had always used every other means before resorting to kill—to accomplish his ends.

The day passed and darkness fell over the vast wilderness around them. With the coming of night, Lawson became nervous. He walked back and forth across the room,

90

from opening on the side of the "window" which led out into the cave, and to the outside. Here he would listen, his ear to the opening. Every crack of a stick, or the fall of a leaf would cause him to move uneasily.

Meanwhile, Wright, detecting this, adjusted himself to the same condition. While Lawson would be at one opening, Wright would be at the other, and they would pass each other in the room. Each kept his hand on his gun.

"I tell you, I'd jump out of this hole and land a thousand feet below before I'd be captured," Jack Lawson declared.

"I don't know, I might, too," Wright said.

"It's awful, such a life as this. I'd rather be dead. But I can't die," Jack Lawson said seriously.

Until far into the night the march across the room continued, while now and then one of them would mend the little fire, so as to have a light.

After the turn of midnight Wright suggested that they lie down. Lawson agreed and gave Wright one of his quilts.

Wright lay on one side of the fire, Lawson on the other, facing each other.

Thus they lay throughout the long hours of the night, hands on guns and eyes wide open.

When the birds began to chatter in the forest around them they rose and prepared their breakfast, then watched the rising sun, as she came up through the dense fog in the valley and shot her rays in through the opening.

Not one minute had either slept the night before. Consequently they felt tough and irritable. But neither wished to go to sleep.

And so when Lawson suggested that they go and kill a deer, Wright was pleased. The thought came to him that he might have an opportunity to capture Lawson. But this thought was promptly dispersed from his mind. He had fully decided that Lawson would never consent to arrest—alive. And he didn't want to kill him. And so there

91

remained only one remedy. He would pit his energy and endurance against those of Lawson, and see who won.

A deer was killed soon after they had left the cave. A hind quarter was taken out and carried to the cave and they feasted the rest of the day.

When night came again, Lawson was as nervous as he had been the previous night. But his pace was slower, and he talked little. For an hour, they both walked around, Wright trying to appear more nervous than the other.

This time, at Lawson's suggestion, they lay down again in the same manner they had occupied the last night.

At two o'clock in the morning both were awake. Wright had questioned the other a little about what he had done, but seeing he did not want to talk about it, refrained from further talk on the subject. On the other hand, Wright had told him of several crimes he had committed, hoping to draw him out.

Wright began to snore, and it was with great difficulty that he kept from falling to sleep while trying to appear so. But he revived and kept a close watch on Lawson. The light of the little fire shone on the other's face and hands, though dim it was.

Now, John Wright saw the grip of Lawson's hand slowly relax from his gun then catch again, hold a few seconds and fall a little farther down. Meanwhile, Wright detected the other's heavy breathing. Finally his hand fell down by his side, while his breathing became deep and heavy.

Wright lay for a few minutes, to make sure that Lawson was asleep, then he slowly removed a pair of handcuffs from under his shirt.

Now with a revolver in one hand, the handcuffs in the other, he eased over, on his hands and knees, until he was bending over Lawson. Like a flash he clipped the cuffs on one hand, threw it across the other and clipped it, picked up the revolver which Lawson had been holding and jerked his other one from the holster.

But the loss of sleep had wearied Lawson so that this did not fully awaken him. His eyes partly opened and fell back.

It was not long until daylight, so Wright decided to let his prisoner rest and sleep, since they could not travel through that wilderness in the dark.

When morning came, Wright prepared breakfast completely and then awoke his prisoner. Then he shook him heavily. Lawson opened his eyes and started to rub them, but found that his hands were shackled together.

Suddenly he became conscious of his condition.

"What'n hell! *You!*"

He sprang from his little bed and made at Wright. His eyes sparkled fire and his jaws looked to be granite.

"What'n hell does this mean?" he stormed.

"Well, Jack—Jack Lawson—you're wanted back home for the wanton murder of your cousin, and for burning his store and taking all the cash you could find. Now, if you'll eat a bite, we'll be on our way."

"I thought that when that old crazy galoot brought you here. I wanted to kill you then. And why didn't I? I almost made up my mind to kill you here. What caused me not to do it?" Then he strode toward the outside opening, looked down, as if he might take a plunge. Wright was ready to prevent it if he had tried. However, apparently he had changed his mind.

"Yes, pal," Wright said calmly, "I know you wanted to kill me. But you never had *one* chance from the time I came in sight of you. Nor did you have one here in this room. But there were several times when I could have killed you before you could have brought your gun from leather. I didn't come to kill you. I want the *law* to do that."

Lawson dropped his head for a moment, as if cowed in spirit and soul. Then he raised it and asked:

"Now, do you care to tell me your name?"

93

"I'm John Wright," he answered. "To my friends, I'm known as 'Bad' John, and to my enemies, 'Devil' John."

"Well, I've heard a lot about you, and now I *know* a lot about you, Wright," Lawson said bitterly. "You're slick, and if I had knowed that you was John Wright, nobody would've knowed where you was buried."

Wright laughed, then said, "I say, *eat,* so we can get out of this jungle, which you said you hate so much."

Back at old Brayley's, Wright apologized for his unethical method of finding and capturing Lawson, Brayley's nephew. He kept a keen eye on the old mountaineer, meanwhile. In Brayley's eyes Wright saw his own end, should he give him an opportunity.

Wright put Lawson in the saddle, and he climbed up behind him. Then they began the long ride back, joining Wright's deputy friend and his aid at the appointed place, where Wright released the prisoner.

John Wright, about a year before his death, stated this as being his greatest piece of detective work. It afforded him more opportunity to use his ability along the line of criminal detection than any other during his whole life.

Chapter X

Murder of Linvil Higgins

For the love of money and the satisfying of old grudges, many innocent men had been reported for liquor violations from the vast Beaver Creek Valley. Much of this territory was later to become Knott County. And there were guilty ones reported by others more guilty than they. As already stated in another chapter, "'portin'" took Dick Vance to Catlettsburg and came close to bringing about his death. A mistake in Vance's identity by one of Hall's men, and quick thinking on Vance's part, saved his life, but caused the death of a friend, John Adams, of Letcher County.

Upon Vance's return home, it is alleged that he, Andy Slone, and Linvil Higgins waylaid and shot Andy Hall, brother of Talt Hall, and son of Bill Dee Hall, as Andy Hall climbed a fence with a sack of potatoes on his back. Andy Hall had, said Vance, been one of the four who attempted Vance's murder at Catlettsburg.

Bill Dee Hall was a quiet, peaceable man who tried to keep out of the troubles of his neighbors, but his sons were very active. When the news of so cruel a death as Andy Hall had suffered reached him, all mountaineers would expect the father's response with rifle and revolver. Then, when the news of the death of Linvil Higgins, reportedly one of the men who had shot Andy Hall from the fence, was spread over the countryside, no one was surprised. However, tradition says that Bill Dee Hall did not kill Linvil Higgins, nor was he connected with it in any way. But if Bill Dee Hall rejoiced in Higgins's death, no one can blame him if another had wreaked vengeance for him.

According to eyewitnesses, Higgins was being fired upon by three men as he ran from them. Only one of the men, Wash Craft, was positively identified. The other two were suspected as being Sam Wright, brother of John Wright, and Ben Jones.

Warrants were sworn out promptly at Hindman for the three suspects. Dolph Draughan, a deputy sheriff, took the warrants and organized a posse to go to Letcher County, to arrest Craft, Wright, and Jones.

Draughan, knowing the cunning and courage of "Old Clabe" Jones, approached the manchaser and leader of a clan, and asked him to lead the party into Letcher County.

Jones raised heavy gray brows, his sharp gray eyes moving slowly from one to another of the twenty-odd hard-looking mountaineers. Every man had a pistol on his hip, and a rifle across the pommel of his saddle. It was apparent at once to Draughan that Jones would decline the invitation.

"You men aim to *ride* to Letcher?" Clabe inquired.

"How else?" Draughan replied sharply. "Think we're gonna *walk* forty miles?"

Jones shook his almost-white head in a semi-circle.

"If you know'd ol' John Wright like I do, you'd crawl there on your bellies and be sure you got there in the dark," Clabe told him. "You won't get your men."

"Well, we ain't doin' no crawling," Draughan declared with emphasis. Then, he ordered his men to proceed toward Letcher County.

Old Clabe's smile, as he watched them gallop out of sight, was one of pity.

Next morning at dawn, the Draughan party rode out of

the mouth of Millstone Creek of Kentucky River and turned up the North Fork, towards the home of Sam Wright.

Within a few minutes the party drew up near the big Wright home, where John, Sam, Martin, and the rest had been born and brought up. Draughan observed the surroundings cautiously. The home was of hewed logs, built in two sections. The underpart was one story, whereas, the top section was of two-story construction, facing the road.

A heavy smoke rose from the stovepipe, and the only sounds were those of pots and pans in the kitchen. It was yet early, barely daylight.

"We'll charge it by storm," Draughan ordered importantly. "The men are eating breakfast. Not expecting a raid, of course they failed to put out a guard. Let's go!"

They dashed forward to the fence, sprang from their mounts, climbed the fence and charged up to the door. Meanwhile, Martha Jane, Sam Wright's small, dark-complexioned wife, heard the running horses and arrived at the door in time to greet them. Some of the men were still trying, in their fright and excitement, to get off their horses, or to climb over the fence. One man had gotten a foot hung in a stirrup and was unable to free himself. Finally he kicked loose and joined the others. Guns were held in position and Draughan demanded a search of the premises.

"You're welcome," Martha Jane Wright told them.

They ran into the house, looked under the beds, behind pieces of furniture and in every spot where a man might hide. Finally, not finding a man person, Draughan told his men to set the ladder up to the opening to the upstairs.

The excited men shuffled about, some of them shaking so badly they could scarcely hold the ladder or climb it.

A search of the upstairs revealed nothing. Then the men stamped about the door, disappointed—or pleased—at their failure to find the men for whom they hunted.

97

Martha Jane Wright was amused throughout the proceedings. She had remained silent while the search was in process. But now, while the men's morale was at a low ebb, she began to speak. She looked at certain ones, whom she knew, and whose records she knew.

"*You*," she said calmly, indicating Draughan, the leader. "What are *you* doing here?"

"We've got warrants to arrest Sam Wright, Wash—"

"*You?*" Martha Jane interrupted. "*You*, Dolph Draughan, a murderer, carrying warrants for others? What about Press Day? You remember him, don't you? You know—the man you murdered on Carr's Fork?"

"Now, see here—"

"And you," Martha interrupted, pointing out the giant with long whiskers, the man who had gotten hung in the stirrup. "Don't you know that I could have killed you while you played with your stirrup?"

From him, she indicated another and another, calling them by their names.

"You gang of outlaws," Martha Jane said, waving a small hand over all of them. "In the first place, you wouldn't have come here if you hadn't known my husband was away. And if you'd thought there was *one* man upstairs, a swarm of hornets couldn't have chased you up there." She paused, her keen eyes flashing over the score of rough men.

"Well, it's been a good show," she said, humorously. "Now, if you're not afraid my husband will return before you get away, I'll prepare your breakfast. Even murderers get hungry."

Some of the men smiled sheepishly, others looked at her with contempt.

Defeated and disgusted, Draughan directed his men back down the river, toward Millstone Creek where, within the hour, they were to encounter "Bad" John Wright, Sam Wright, and the clan, in the "Daniel's Hill Fight."

98

Chapter XI

Daniel's Hill Fight

On the night that Dolph Draughan led a party from Knott County, John Wright, Sam Wright, Wash Craft, and their followers left the home of Sam Wright, anticipating a raid from Knott County. These men understood that there were warrants out for Sam Wright, Wash Craft, and Ben Jones for the killing of Linvil Higgins, near Hindman.

Knowing the enmity that existed between the factions in Knott County and his own men, John Wright, leader of the Letcher Countians, feared that a group led by Clabe Jones would never take the men in alive. John Wright did not know that Jones had refused to accompany Draughan and his men, else the outcome might have been different.

Therefore, rifles and revolvers were inspected, cleaned, and operated to see that they were in perfect order. The old enmity which Clabe Jones had instilled into John Wright back at the beginning of the war, when Jones argued with the Wright family and in a flame of sudden anger he took John's horse from him in the field—these things flamed anew within him when he thought that Jones might arrest his brother Sam, then kill him on the way to prison.

Not wishing an encounter at the home of Sam Wright, or

99

any other home where women and children might be in danger, John Wright directed his men down Kentucky River, afoot, of course.

It was a moonless night in early Autumn of 1885, the air cool and pleasant. Several such nights they had already spent, scouting for the enemy and, although threats had been sent from Knott County, John feared those threats were unfounded, for now he wished a showdown, an opportunity to come face to face with Clabe Jones and see which one would be left.

At midnight, they came to the mouth of Millstone Creek, and being worn from loss of sleep and the days and nights of restless scouting, they went into the home of "Uncle" Bee Craft, father of Wash Craft, to rest. As soon as they got settled in the home they began to fall over asleep. Then John Wright, despairing of the probability of the band coming from Knott County that night, insisted that they all go to bed and get some rest.

Mrs. Craft at once protested, saying it would be dangerous. However she was overcome and soon every man was sleeping soundly.

They had slept scarcely two hours when Mrs. Craft rushed into the room.

"Boys!" she exclaimed. "John—Wash!"

The men sprang up, seized their rifles, thinking the enemy already there.

"Get out of here!" she demanded. "I told you not to go to bed here. Wash!"

There was something ominous in her tone.

"I tell you—get out quick! I just feel it, I seen it in a dream, a vision, for I wasn't asleep. They're comin'. We'll all be killed—"

The elderly woman wrung her hands in desperation, walking back and forth until the last man had left the house.

100

When they had emerged, she still walked the floor, praying audibly—

"My God, my God!"

John, knowing by personal experience, and the experience of others, that the old people of the mountains were shown in visions and dreams important events, good or bad, which were soon to come to pass, led his men across the river and they lay in the semi-darkness until the gray dawn. They had not long to wait, for it was nearing daybreak when they arrived across the stream.

As the first ray of light shone from the east, the sound of horses' feet was heard. The riders were coming down Millstone. Wright and his men were too far away from the road for an encounter here, so they lay still and listened to the party coming out of Millstone and go up Kentucky River. The riders' forms were vaguely visible in the gray dawn, a long, single column, riding at a moderate gait. Their voices could be heard, but not understood.

"Now—to Daniel's Hill!" John Wright ordered.

John Wright had every reason to believe that Draughan (or Clabe Jones, as he thought) was leading his men to Sam Wright's, where they expected to find Sam, Wash Craft, and Ben Jones, unaware, and slaughter them wholesale. But failing to find them there, the party would hurry next to Bee Craft's, their second chance to find the men.

Daniel's Hill is a long, protruding ridge which forces the river into a horseshoe bend a short distance above Millstone Creek. It was here that Daniel Boone camped and cut his initials on a beech tree, which initials were blocked out and taken to a museum. The road, instead of following the river, a long distance around, cut across the ridge to save mileage, though it necessitated two crossings of the river.

John Wright estimated the time it would take the Knott County party to go to Sam's, make a search and return by

Daniel's Hill. Feeling sure that they had sufficient time, they walked slowly up the river, planning the attack.

The men were to form into three groups along the side of the hill. John, with the largest number of men, was to command the center of the attack, shielded behind the rise in front of a large sinkhole. Sam was to take some of the men and form the front line, which would open the attack, some hundred yards above, as the party approached, while the third, generaled by Wash Craft, was to take a stand just below John's command and make it hot for the retreating enemies.

However, John's estimation fell short, owing no doubt, to the disgust of Draughan and his party upon their failure to find the men at Sam Wright's. They had ridden harder on the return, heading for Bee Craft's, where they had expected to take their men.

Consequently Wright's men were just reaching Daniel's Hill when they heard the other party crossing the river above.

"Quick—to the bushes!" John Wright ordered.

There was hustling for cover, each man trying to find a bush or a log to use as a breastwork, for there were no large trees close enough for them to reach. Soon the men formed a long row around the hillside, some seventy-five yards from where the raiders must cross the river, the ford which entered the hill.

"When they get straight under—shoot!" John whispered to his men.

The Knott County posse galloped over the top of the ridge, then down the slope and into the river, slowing down when they reached the water. The river at this point is merely a large creek, requiring only a few seconds to cross it.

As the party plunged into the shallow water, kicking and spurring their horses and murmuring and cursing, a long line of rifles and revolvers raised steadily to the

102

shoulders of the men on the hill, almost vertical, above the prey. When the oncoming riders were well into the water, the guns on the hill belched fire and horses surged, while some of the men sprang off and took shelter behind rocks and logs, and began returning the fire. Dolph Draughan's horse fell dead at the sound of the first volley. Draughan sprang behind the dead animal, using him as a barricade, and started firing at the men on the hill.

One of the Draughan party seized his chest and turned his horse up the river, and speeded out of sight. Another seized his thigh. It was apparent that the men were panic-stricken—as Martha Jane Wright had predicted, should they encounter her husband and his companions. They were running, jumping, trying to find a place for protection.

But a few still peppered the lead up the hill from behind stones and other obstructions near the river.

Finally, seeing they had no chance against the Wright men, they fled in confusion.

Then John Wright called his men and ascertained whether anybody had been wounded. All answered that nothing had hit them except the wind from the passing slugs of lead. Then, to their surprise, John Wright explained that he had been wounded in the shoulder.

"Not many people know to this day that I was wounded at the Daniel's Hill fight," John Wright told this (senior) writer forty-five years after the fight. "It was reported that Talt Hall was wounded, but that was false. It was me."

John Wright regretted the killing of Dolph Draughan's horse. It was not the custom of any of the clans to kill horses. Horses were the friends of everybody, and the instructions always were to kill the enemy, but not his horse. It was said that John Wright apologized to Draughan later for the horse, and paid him for it, though this was disputed.

After the Draughan men had fled, John and his party followed them. As they rode up the river, they met Martin Wright, one of John's brothers, who was then magistrate. Martin had been to get a doctor for a neighbor. He and the doctor had ridden along with the Draughan party until they came close to the Hill, then suspecting trouble, they had lagged behind, letting the men pass. Soon they had heard the shooting and in a few minutes the man who had left the scene and ridden fast up the river, dashed his horse up to Martin Wright.

"Here!" the wounded man exclaimed, offering his pistol to the magistrate. "Arrest me, try me, take me to jail—anything!"

Martin Wright refused to arrest him. The doctor looked him over and saw that his wound was not serious, and advised him to go somewhere where attention could be given to it.

John Wright and his men chased the Draughan party out of Letcher County into Knott County. However, John's wound in the shoulder became too painful for him to continue with the men, so he returned. On the retreat, Draughan and his clan were faster than on the attack, so they escaped to their own land.

Chapter XII

Clabe Jones Attacks Fort Wright

When Clabe Jones and his clan returned from several days' scouting in Letcher County and learned that John Wright, Talt Hall, and their factions had been in Knott County, searching for them, "Old Clabe" was furious. He led his band quickly back to Letcher County.

They traveled night and day, keeping away from all trails, until they came near Elkhorn valley. They were now in enemy country. They lay up during the day, cooking their lunches over little fires. Sentinels were posted on all sides, and Jones's field glasses were used to search the open spaces and forest lanes.

They entered the headwaters of Elkhorn at midnight. From there, absolute silence was maintained. The band now scattered, so as not to make more than one track in a place. Old logs and fallen trees, rocks and hard surfaces were walked over to break the signs. Finally they came to the wagon trail, where Clabe stopped them abruptly.

"Every one of you get a rock," Clabe ordered. "The first one reaching the road, put your rock down and step on it. The ones behind, give your rocks to the ones ahead and lay them down, stepping on them. *Never* step on the ground! When the rocks are laid plumb across the road, each man is to walk on them. The last man to cross, pick up the rocks behind, throw them into the woods. We're in John Wright country."

The leader's instructions were followed religiously and all crossed the road without leaving a single track.

When within two miles of Fort Wright, Jones directed his men towards the creek, which ran through the forest at this point. It was May, and the creek was full from spring rains, and roared and splashed in the silent, black night, so that footsteps were made inaudible, even to these men.

"From here, we wade the creek," Clabe told his followers. "Old John'll never forget this visit."

It was a weary, torturous two miles, stumbling over boulders, falling into the raging stream, descending little falls. Although it was springtime, the fresh waters soon became cold, finally chilling the men to their bones. Some of them cursed silently, but gripped tightly their new rifles, and kept their heavy revolvers above water. All were eager to try the modern rifles on the Wright-Hall clan.

At dawn, they came within sight of "Fort Wright." Jones searched the surroundings with his powerful glasses. But there were no signs of men around "Mattie's House."

Then Jones directed his men to proceed to the "Striped House," just below the fort. It was here at the small house that Jones expected to find the men he wanted.

Breakfast was over at the Striped House and John Wright had gone to work in the field, below. He had taken along his eighty-dollar shotgun, the only one of its kind in the mountains. Sam Wright, who owned a steam mill over on Kentucky River, but who was afraid to operate it alone, was working in the yard at the Striped House, on an old bolting chest, a part of the flour-making apparatus to his mill, anticipating, when the Jones-Wright-Hall war was over, to start the mill again. The other members of the band were milling around or lounging in the house.

Since their trip to Knott County and their failure to find Jones and his clan, the Wright-Hall men had grown lax in their vigilance, not yet having learned Clabe Jones's tactics in feudist warfare. They had succeeded in making themselves believe that Old Clabe would not return again, and, if he should, it would not be soon. This, however, was contrary to John Wright's belief. He had cautioned them daily ever to be alert for the appearance of Jones.

Talt Hall, Bill Hawk Sizemore, Bill Bates, and Wash Craft sauntered around to where Sam Wright was working, intending to assist, if he would allow it. But suddenly the ground opened up in several places around them, followed by the sharp crack of strange rifles—sounds they had never heard before. Slugs whistled by their ears, brushed their clothing.

Wright's men jerked their revolvers and began firing back into the forest, whence the shots were coming. Sam Wright climbed the paling fence, starting toward his brother, John, who had the shotgun—and the security, he thought. As he reached the top of the fence, a slug plowed into one of the sharp-pointed palings, spattering splinters over him. He jumped to the ground and ran with all his might to the field—and to John.

Meanwhile, the Jones clan was closing in on the Striped House and the Wright-Hall men were retreating, in the face of flying lead from the new high-power rifles. Bill Hawk Sizemore, Bill Dee Hall, and Miles Bates were cornered and captured.

Now the Jones band was chasing Talt Hall, Wash Craft, Bill Bates, and others, who were firing back at them as they ran. No one ever questioned the fact that the Hall men were suffering severe defeat.

However, just as the Jones men was closing in on the remainder of the clan, John Wright came in sight, his shotgun belching flames and pellets. "Bad" John was now in his most dangerous mood. He took aim on each prey, his gray, dark eyes sighting down the barrel steadily. Pine Mountain roared, as if the atom bomb had been discovered years ahead of its time.

Clabe Jones sprang behind a tree and aimed at John, but the latter, whose glance took in the whole situation, opened again. The bark shattered around Clabe's face and he withdrew.

"Run for your lives!" Clabe told the men. "But hold them prisoners at any cost!" he yelled to those he had trusted to take the captured men up the creek.

John Wright's shotgun continued to roar, sending buckshots through the forest, and purring past the fleeing men.

Strange, but actually true, not a man was wounded in the fight except that some of them were frightened almost to death. Some of the Hall men had run off and John Wright had difficulty in getting them together again. Finally, after corraling them, he set them on the trail of Jones. But after following the clan for several miles, Wright's men gave up, and called it a draw. Or was it? Clabe had captured three of Wright's men, and was taking them to prison.

Jones arrived with his prisoners at Hindman late in the day. Here, he would keep the captured men until morning, when he would deliver them to Prestonsburg for trial.

Soon after his arrival, Dolph Draughan, supposedly a deputy sheriff, came to Jones in an angry mood. This is the same Dolph Draughan who had directed the "Daniel's Hill fight," and lost; the same Draughan with whom Clabe had refused to go on a childish raid; the Draughan whom Martha Jane Wright had ridiculed and shamed at her home.

Draughan was jealous and resentful because Old Clabe's

108

warning to him had been sound, and now Clabe had proved it by bringing in the prisoners.

"I want them prisoners," Draughan demanded.

Clabe Jones's gray eyes narrowed as the old clan leader studied Draughan.

"You want to kill 'em, Draughan," Clabe replied calmly. "You went to Letcher to kill 'em, but they outwitted you. I went to capture them, and I got them. They're my prisoners, and nobody gets 'em. I'm taking them to jail tomorrow."

Draughan turned to his men and ordered them to line up in a firing squad.

"Now, are you gonna give 'em up?" Draughan asked, as the men formed.

Jones didn't answer, but said to his men: "Line up in front of these prisoners, and I'll be in front of you." Then to Draughan he said, "Make one move and it'll be the last of your murdering band."

Draughan, defeated again, took his men away without speaking another word.

This phase of the raid, like many another concerning the old days, was disputed by some.

Ten days followed; days of anxiety, fear, hate at white heat. The powerful talons of outlawry had spread their sharp claws over the valleys and on the mountains, clutching at the throat of everyone. No one was safe, regardless of how careful he was, for in the midst of all opposing clans were men without conscience, without character, who were eager to use the clan as a cloak under which they might hide to wreak vengeance upon innocent persons whom they did not like for very trivial reasons. With some, there was no such thing as neutrality. One must be enemy or friend; there was no middle ground.

Daniel Boone, when he camped at the forks of Kentucky River, lived in no more dread of the red men than did the honest people of the mountains during the hectic years recorded in this book. Different methods of precaution were employed. Some barred their doors at night, advising any guests who might be spending the night not to open the door until morning. Others lay in their dark cabins, with doors wide open, believing that no sensible man would enter a dark doorway, knowing that persons were within, ready to shoot at any moment.

It was at this crucial time that Sam Wright, Wash Craft, Talt Hall, and others of the John Wright clan were persuaded to leave the mountains. John Wright knew that if the crime wave continued, nobody could win. In the end, he would fall, as many had fallen from his own gun and those of his clansmen. He called his men together. His flashing gray eyes centered first on Talt Hall.

"Talt," he began calmly, but firmly. He paused, and the men grew closer around him, for there was something in his tone they had never heard before. "Talton, I've protected you since the day I persuaded Captain Williams not to kill you. My doors have never been closed to you. I've given you shelter, food, and protection, the same as my family."

Talt's eyes widened as the tall leader paused and looked down into them. Talt's red mustache apparently became more conspicuous as he listened intently.

"Now, Talt, you'll have to go," John Wright declared with resolution.

"Go!" Talt exclaimed, stiffening. "Go where? Think I'm gonna let Old Clabe Jones run me from home?"

"No," John Wright said a bit sharply. "I don't intend to give Clabe time. I'm going to take you myself—not from your home, because you have no home, but from these mountains. At least, you're leaving Letcher County. I'd suggest Virginia."

Talt looked toward Pound Gap, the historic pass leading into the Old Dominion.

Then John Wright pointed a long, slender finger at Wash Craft, a tall, handsome, dark man of about twenty-six years.

"Wash, you and Sam (John's brother) go in another direction. This trouble must stop. It never will as long as you fellers stay here."

There were shuffling of feet, fidgeting, uncertainty, and puzzlement.

"Sam, you and Wash go together and stay together. Either one of you would get lost alone out of these mountains. And *stay*! Stay somewhere until things quiet down around here, then I'll let you know that it's safe to return. Let us know, somehow, where you are, but be careful how you do it."

Martha Jane Wright, Sam's wife, had risen above her love for her husband, and had been pleading for him to leave, knowing that loneliness would surely be hers in his absence. But Sam had refused her, telling Martha Jane that he would rather die than to separate from his family. However, John Wright was a leader of mountain men. They saw his logic and common sense, and agreed to depart *now*.

John Wright longed for the day that lasting peace would reign in the Pine Mountain area. He knew that it would take some time for things to cool down, but how long? He wondered! Coal developments had opened the way for inquisitive strangers immigrating into Letcher County. Some became friends, some cruel outlaws.

The hot summer temperature was somewhat cooled with the evening shade, as the sun had just settled over the tall rugged mountains. Squawking sounds of the fouls of the air mingling with the ripple of the flowing streams were suddenly silenced by the stamping of horses feet amidst the darkness of the tall pines. Like a coon hunting hound, John could scent the very sound of trouble, the kind John was hoping had ended.

111

Demanding voices could be heard as he cautiously approached the scene. "What ye got thar, stranger?" Then an answer very politely: "I sell best 'murchan-dise' . . . will be very pleased to show you gen-tle-men."

"Listen, stranger! Here you don't sell, and we don't buy. We take!" snapped a demanding voice.

"I don't think you will take . . . not for free," the brave, neatly dressed one answered, as he slowly opened the lid to his carrying case from which shone a flicker of brightness of steel.

At this point John saw the flash of a pistol coming from the holster of one who seemed to be the spokesman of the gang as he stepped down off his horse and unto the ground. Three more remained in their saddles.

Instantly he concluded that the bandits were none of Claybourne Jones's men or Talt Hall's. The Joneses and the Wrights had their differences, but Clabe was a more repentant Clabe Jones now. Not since his early Civil War days had he ever taken advantage of someone who he felt was not his personal enemy.

"Having trouble fellows?" John Wright butted in.

"Oh, just huntin' gold. Any objections?" stormed the one standing, still holding the pistol in his hand. Without waiting for an answer, the bandit's gun barrel swung around and pointed straight toward the valorous stranger. Instantly John answered with the sound of thunder and fire from his hip! It struck the pistol barrel of the intended robber! Only a bloody scratch was visible on the bandit's right hand, as his gun fell to the ground. Another still sitting on his horse, gave a quick jerk with his left hand bringing his revolver about half way out of his holster when Bad John shouted: "Hold it right there buddy! Don't anyone make another move except to hi-tail-it out'a here! This is graveyard country, and I sure would hate to bury you fellows!"

112

At this point the intruders turned their horses around and fled toward Wise County, Virginia.

"Where ye from, stranger?" John inquired of the traveling salesman.

"I come to your country, an—"

What's your name?"

"Frank Darwin," he answered. "You are a gen-tle-man. You help a stranger you not know."

He explained that he had migrated from the Middle East to America during his early boyhood days.

As John turned around he saw a trinkle of blood splattered upon the ground that had dripped from the wounded hand of the outlaw.

"Come go with me," John suggested. "I think you'll be safe for awhile, that is, if you care to put up with Martha and me and them country vittles."

Frank Darwin did become accustomed to John Wright's country "vittles." He later purchased some property and made his home in the mountains where he remained the rest of his life.

In the Cumberlands, as in the "Old West," there were "Glory" seekers who strove to acquire reputations by "downing" noted bad men. These conscienceless killers were eager to effect this transfer of notoriety by gunning famous fighters in the twilight of their careers.

One such belligerent ruffian, reputedly a member of the gang thwarted by Wright in attempts to rob Frank Darwin, accosted John in the Jenkins mine office.

"So you are Bad John Wright, and claim you killed fourteen men!"

"I could make if fifteen in another minute!" Wright replied to the challenge. The stranger blenched visibly— and hurriedly left.

John Wright remained, perhaps a bit older, but still indomitable.

Chapter XIII

The Peace Conference

Martha Jane Wright, small, keen-eyed, intelligent, opened the once-a-week mail pouch with eager fingers and anxious heart. Sam Wright, her husband, Wash Craft, Talt Hall, and others had been gone from the mountains four months. Not a line had she received from him, nor did she know where he might be. Sam Wright was postmaster of the small *Wright* post office, located in the big Wright house on North Fork of Kentucky River. Whether Sam was at home or away, Martha Jane attended to the post office.

Sam Wright, Wash Craft, and those accused with them in the killing of Linvil Higgins, in Knott County, had been persuaded, or forced by John Wright, the clan leader, to leave until matters could be cleared up.

The post office work, small as it was, gave Martha Jane Wright some diversion from the drabness and loneliness that besieged the great Wright home, even though the mail carrier came only once a week. The months had seemed ages, until one day, a day she would never forget, when a newspaper rolled out of the pouch onto the table. It was addressed to "The Postmaster." The writing—it was her husband's!

But a newspaper! she thought with pounding heart. It

114

Mrs. Sam Wright (Martha Jane Wright) and son Washie.
Photograph made about 1909.

could mean only one thing—Sam was in jail, and the paper
was giving an account of the crime he had committed.

"Mother" Wright, Sam's mother, stood close to Martha
Jane, as she did on the arrival of every mail, hoping for
word from her son.

A sheet of writing paper unfolded when Martha Jane
tore off the wrapper.

115

"Mother!" she exclaimed. "It's from Sam!"

Her eyes flashed across the page, as she was an excellent reader, one of the best educated women in the mountains.

"Mother," she repeated, "Sam's well, and he's had a change of heart. He quotes the Twenty-third Psalm." She began to read it, as Mother Wright settled into a chair, head bowed low.

"The Lord is my Shepherd; I shall not want.

"He maketh me to lie down in green pastures; he leadeth me beside still waters.

"He restoreth my soul; he leadeth me in the paths of righteousness for his name's sake.

"Yea, though I walk through the valley of the shadow of death, I will fear no evil; for thou art with me; thy rod and thy staff they comfort me.

"Thou preparest a table before me in the presence of mine enemies; thou anointest my head with oil; my cup runneth over.

"Surely goodness and mercy shall follow me all the days of my life; and I will dwell in the house of the Lord forever."

Before the final words were read, great drops were trickling down the elder woman's cheeks. Then she said, almost inaudibly.

"May God end it all."

"No, Mother," Martha Jane said confidently. "The Lord did not bring on this crime and bloodshed. Our own people did it, and *we* have to stop it. If we'll try, God will give us strength and wisdom, and the Holy Spirit will be with us daily. But now we have to start to work—you and I and every peace-loving citizen in these mountains."

Martha Jane Wright did start to work. Rather, she intensified her efforts, which she had been putting forth over several months.

First, she sent for John Wright, her husband's brother,

116

and leader of the Letcher County clan, the Wright side of the Wright-Jones vendetta.

John Wright, already tired of fighting, of chasing bands and being chased over the hills, was eager for peace.

Next, Martha Jane sent word to "Uncle" Bee Craft, father of Wash Craft, who was with Sam Wright—somewhere. Bee Craft, an elderly and peaceful man, was ready to do all he could to effect peace.

Who else? Martha Jane didn't have long to put her thoughts on the next man to call into the conference. He was "Black" Shade Combs, so-called because of his dark complexion. Combs had, through the years of fighting, been a true friend of every member of both factions, always pleading for sanity and common sense. He was *one* man who could visit any members of any faction in the mountains, spend nights with them, yet never be suspected. Even his fine build, his walk, his manner, his voice were in his favor, so that there was never a danger of his identification being mistaken.

Martha Jane sent for Shade Combs to appear at her home along with John Wright, Bee Craft, and others. This was in the early spring of 1886. When they were assembled on her broad and greening lawn, Martha Jane spoke, her gentle but firm words piercing the hearts of her listeners:

"Men, judging from your actions since the Civil War ended, you're not human, but devils in the flesh. And that goes for Clabe Jones and his Knott County band and, especially for Talt Hall and his clan. My husband and others were forced to leave their homes. Why? They're just as guilty as any of you. The urge to conquer, the will to dominate his fellowmen, and pride, man's worst enemy —these are back of all this crime wave in our beautiful mountains, which God gave us to use for another purpose. Honest, hardworking men have been transformed into

117

demons without conscience, bent on eliminating all who don't agree with them and who don't *obey* them."

Martha Jane paused and, during the intense silence, her eyes flashed from one face to another. Every man there knew that she had cast a spell over him—a spell he loved. Overhead, meanwhile, the silver-throats of a thrush floated down to them, soothing and *peaceful.* The great shade trees cast an invigorating coolness about them.

"You're not devils," Martha Jane said, awaking them from their reverie. "You're still human, but within your souls are demons that are directing your lives. Some of you fight these devilish forces some of the time, others all the time, but you *never surrender* to the still small voice that speaks to you daily. You're *capable* of becoming *men* again, or of going on and wrecking, forever, our mountain homeland, the only we've ever known or ever will know. You're continuing to furnish the mercenary writers of the big cities with material to brand you, and *correctly,* as outlaws.

"It matters not who started these feuds," she continued in her calm, gentle manner. "That question will never be settled, for none of you will admit to the truth. What *does* matter to us and the children we're bringing up, is *future peace.* Now, we want to know whether you're going to be *men* or devils in the years ahead. Are you willing to stack away your high-powers and revolvers, relieve your shoulders and your hips of that heavy load, a load that brings still a heavier load upon your heart and upon the hearts of your children and grandchildren? We all know that back of all your fighting and killing, there's still honor within everyone of you. We'll trust your word. Tell us just where you stand."

Then she indicated the Letcher County clan leader.

"First, you, John Wright. Do you want peace, or bloodshed to continue?"

John Wright, tall, slender, straight, rose quickly from his seat.

"I'm for anything that's right," he said. "Anything—"

"But who's to say what's right?" Martha Jane interrupted. "You or Clabe Jones, or Talt Hall? Both you and Clabe are honest at heart, wanting to do what's right. But your opinions differ on that point. Are you willing to let the *people* say what's right?"

John Wright hesitated, looked over the small crowd, his eyes settling on "Mother" Wright, his own mother, who was drying her eyes with a gingham apron.

"I'll see that my men stop going to Knott County," he promised. "And if some of them do go and get into trouble, I'll take them to jail. I'll meet Clabe Jones anywhere, without guns, and talk it over."

Martha Jane spoke to Shade Combs then, asking his opinion.

"I'll see Clabe," Combs promised. "But I know that he will agree. He's as tired of it all as any of you. It's only a matter of pride. Surrender *that* and you'll strike old Clabe in the heart. I'll take Clabe's word for anything, the same as I'll accept John Wright's."

"Now, Uncle Bee," Martha Jane said to Bee Craft. "Are you willing—"

"Anything, anything," the elder Mr. Craft hurried to promise. "You all know I've never wanted anything but peace."

"There's one condition," Shade Combs explained. "That's Talt Hall. John Wright, you know the enmity that stands between Clabe Jones and Talt. As long as you protect Talt, we can never win Clabe Jones for peace. What about it?"

"I've protected him, yes," John Wright admitted. "I've fought for him and fed him, because I liked him. I still like him. I'm still his friend, and will help him if he'll try to help himself. But Talt's gone now, and if he returns and starts

119

trouble, I won't protect him. He'll have to fight his own battles."

"That's all the promise I need," Shade Combs replied. "I'll take the news to Clabe Jones, and return at once with his decision."

James Claybourne Jones or "Old Clabe," had been a bad man from childhood, according to his own words, written by himself, and published (and possibly revised) by J. W. Hall, of Hazard, Perry County, Kentucky: "Clabe," he states, "even when a mere boy, how many men he killed, no man knew but himself—even if he knew. He had killed, robbed, and pillaged during the Civil War, according to his own admission. But there was one good quality which he had always possessed. His word was as good as a gold bond." John Wright knew this, and was willing to take the Knott County leader's promise for peace.

The old leader shrugged his broad shoulders, thrust back his shock of white hair and grinned happily when "Black" Shade Combs told him his mission to Clabe's home.

"Well, I reckon if they've got enough fighting, I have," he replied.

"Then you're willing to quit and persuade your men to, like John Wright?" Combs insisted.

"Yeah," Clabe said, his half-closed gray eyes apparently flashing his words into Combs's heart. "I won't go to Letcher, or let my men. If some of John's men come over here and get into trouble, and John don't protect them, I'll take no part in it."

"That's all I ask, Clabe," Combs said, and left at once for Letcher County. When a few yards away, Combs turned his horse and called back to Clabe:

"I'll take your word and John Wright's for anything. The war's over."

Then he waved goodbye, and saw the happy smile on the old warrior's face as a big hand waved in response.

Not only did Shade Combs continue to carry messages from John Wright to Clabe Jones, and vice versa, but the peacemaker visited important and strong followers of each leader. In the weeks that followed, he and Martha Jane Wright relaxed not their efforts. There were some who, though trusting the word of Wright and Jones, knew that there were thoroughly bad characters following each of them, and these would rather carry on as they had through a terrible decade. To them it was fun and often paid off in some form. Without an enemy to ambush, a home to ransack or burn, what diversion could they find? Such as these might manufacture lies and carry them to their leaders, rekindling the old fires, to start another conflagration.

Sam Wright was notified of the proceedings and the peace agreement, and he returned home, after several months' absence. Although the firing had ceased for the time being, the smoke still clung to the valleys and mountainsides; it could be smelled and seen. Doors were still barred in some houses, while others left their doors open all night. Rifles were kept standing by beds and revolvers rested under pillows. Whenever a member of one of the clans would come into the midst of those of another, his hand would instinctively rise to and rest on the butt of his revolver. Although openly friendly, each watched every action of the other with guarded interest. Busy talebearers carried the elusive stories from clan to clan, from member to member, in the hope of reviving the destruction of human lives.

But the leaders, each having pride in his honor and in his word, cautioned daily the members of his clan. Slowly but surely, the will of the honest people began to take root. The erstwhile enemies grew more friendly, more sociable, until the dread, the fear, the hostile looks upon their faces, which had existed through long years, gradually wore away.

That fall (1886) after John Wright and Clabe Jones each felt that the clans would abide by their agreement for peace, met in Whitesburg, county seat for Letcher County, and spent a night together, in a hotel, without benefit of guns. In fact, they slept together. Throughout most of the night, they talked of the long years of warfare, in the Civil War and their own unnecessary bloodshed in the mountains. They both agreed that those had been "misspent years."

Notwithstanding the cessation of hostilities, and the friendship that had begun to rebuild among the erstwhile warring factions, there was a matter that must be settled *by law*. Sam Wright, Wash Craft, and Ben Jones had been accused of killing Linvil Higgins, near Hindman, in Knott County, which incident necessitated their having to leave the mountains for months. Not only did the friends of Higgins demand their coming to trial for the crime, but they and their own relatives and friends insisted that they go to court and clear it up, one way or another.

In response to these demands, and in keeping with his promise, John Wright escorted his brother, Sam Wright, to Prestonsburg, Floyd County, for trial. Another officer brought Wash Craft to court.

Wash Craft was tried first. When the commonwealth's attorney had finished presenting his evidence, many of the spectators wondered why Craft had not been hanged before then. They were sure that a noose was awaiting him when the trial was finished. Everything from a breach of peace to murder had been proved. Or had it?

But when J. P. Marrs, Whitesburg attorney, rose to the aid of his client, all eyes were upon him. Craft stated that he was forty miles from the scene of the killing on that day; that he was working with Sam Wright.

Sam Wright was next on the stand. Wright corroborated Craft's statements. He was followed by others, all stating, in effect, the same thing.

Sam Wright's case followed, and the same evidence, in defense, was presented. The jury deliberated only a few minutes on each case, returning a verdict of not guilty.

Sam Wright returned home. But Wash Craft, it was said, left the mountains, never to return to live.

Clabe Jones took no part in these trials, happy that John Wright had taken his own brother in for trial. That was another link welded in the peace chain.

Chapter XIV

The Ku Klux Klan

Following the hanging of Dr. Taylor, the Red Fox, following the execution of Talt Hall, the mountain people felt that peace had come at last. They believed that this would end the reign of outlawry which had been rampant since the Civil War. Law and order had come to take their rightful place among the hills; fear and dread of molestation would forever be dispersed from the mountains.

However, this great feeling was to be short-lived. There were those in the upper Elkhorn and Kentucky River valleys, who wished so much that peace might be established permanently that they organized a group which was not only to bring and maintain order, but to make it a way of life. There had been no law within their communities to assure the rights of civilized life. The law in most cases was a joke. Men were tried by their "peers," and it was almost always seen that their peers were just that— the same type of characters, who would never let their fellowmen down. It had been left to Virginia, the Old Dominion, to wring down the curtain on bloodshed and outlawry, committed for the most part by Kentuckians, expanding their borders across Pine Mountain. If this mountain section could not have law legally, then it would

124

have it another way, but law, they were determined to have.

The intentions of these people were genuine, and meant for the good of all peace-loving citizens. But, as is always the case, even in the churches, some bad will get into the group. And as the operations of what became the Ku Klux Klan became more widespread, more of the wrong people came in, finally taking control. The bad ones resorted to stealing, robbing, and finally to murder. When the good citizens who had organized the clan saw what was resulting, they began withdrawing, and soon the whole thing was only a band of outlaws who became a menace to the civilized community.

A majority of the members of the clan were said to have been members of the Reynolds family and their friends. On the other hand, there was the family of W. S. Wright, who opposed the clan from the beginning. It is certain that the clan's work was not the root of the vendetta that built up between the Reynolds and W. S. Wrights, but no doubt it did deepen the rift. Certainly there's no intention on the part of this writer to place the blame on either the Wrights or the Reynolds, for the evil that befell both families; we leave that to Heaven. The two neighbors lived near what is now Seco (a name derived from the Southeast Coal Company which built the coal town there after the incidents here related), several miles east of Whitesburg, county seat of Letcher County. In January 1900, as a result of the feuding that had gone on for a long time, W. S. Wright was killed, allegedly by Noah Reynolds. Noah Reynolds and his brother John were together at the time of the killing.

The two brothers were taken before the grand jury at Whitesburg. But for some reason no indictments were lodged against them. The commonwealth's attorney asked that they be held under bond pending the next court. This was granted.

125

By now the clan had become very active, under the control of the wrong people. In the fall following the killing of W. S. Wright, and while John Reynolds, one of those charged with Wright's death, was teaching school nearby, the clan, or some of its members, were alleged to have gone to the home of Jemima Hall. The Hall woman was the well-to-do widow of Allen Hall. The clan members made a charge upon the home, which resulted in the death of Jemima Hall, and the wounding of a man who was in the house, who later died from the wound. There was another woman in the house, but she escaped without injury.

John Wright, then a deputy sheriff . . . as almost always he was . . . set out to bring to justice all who had taken part in the murders at the Hall home. Several persons were taken to Whitesburg, where they gave bond or went to jail. Reynolds, it appeared, had been at home on the evening of the raid on Jemima Hall, and Creed Potter was at the Reynolds that evening. Creed Potter was John Wright's nephew.

Noah Reynolds, brother of John Reynolds, and author of a booklet titled *Mountain Feuds in Kentucky*, gives his version of the fight that ensued:

> Reynolds (John) and Potter, seeing plenty of fresh signs, turned to the left and were coming around a high point in the mountain. Reynolds and Potter, looking up, saw some of Wright's men coming. John Reynolds said: "Yonder they come!"
>
> About this time gun shots were heard. Reynolds raised his gun, fired and mortally wounded Wm. Wright (Young son of W. S. Wright, whom Noah Reynolds was alleged to have killed), then ran up the spur, taking shelter behind an oak tree. Reynolds would spring in behind his tree, wrench his gun, then spring out and fire. He fired five shots, killing and wounding five men. At this time he received a shot which broke his right arm just below the elbow, disabling him so that he could not use his gun. He left the tree and ran down the hill, leaving his partner to fight by himself. Potter went in pursuit of Reynolds, tracking him by the blood and expecting to find him dead. But Reynolds had reached

the main road and had taken up his stand at Jeff Bentley's for a second fight.

Wm. Wright died at 4:00 o'clock the next morning.

McCoy and Beverly were picked up dead on the ground.

Isaac Mills and Elkins were wounded but recovered.

I was on my way to meet John Reynolds at the head of the river where we had an agreement to meet there. I heard shooting, knew it was a fight and turned back in that direction and met a friend coming after me who said,

"Your brother, John Reynolds is wounded and wants you." I dashed away at full speed, and in fifteen minutes was with him.

My men, hearing the fight, rallied together about twenty of them, and joined me. Reynolds was badly wounded. We carried him up to where I lived on the farm of my uncle Joe Reynolds. I sent for Dr. Joe McQuary.

The doctor said it would be dangerous to force him (my brother) to go to town on account of his present condition. So I said to the sheriff, "If you will trust me I will take care of him, and when the doctor says it will be safe, I will bring him to town."

On this he agreed, and I was sworn in and given a written statement showing my authority.

"Devil" John Wright, on hearing this, got very angry and told the sheriff that I didn't intend to bring John Reynolds in, and had taken advantage of him. He asked the sheriff to countermand the order, but the sheriff could not.

Noah Reynolds wrote fully of the whole incident, from the fight to the trials. Next he tells of "The Next Move He Made."

There was what we called a pistol deputy sheriff, one of them John Elkins, who mustered fifteen men, and said they would come and take my wounded brother, John, to town. As I watched for them, I picked up my winchester rifle, walked to the front yard and stepped to the side of the apple tree. As they rode up I raised my gun to my shoulder and said,

"Have you men lived as long as you want to? If you have, the one that want to die first start to get down."

"We don't want any trouble," was the answer.

I said, "If you don't, ride on down the road."

So they went on down the road, thinking I had several men in the background.

Alex Wright, who was friendly with both sides, came and said,

"Noah, I don't take any sides in this trouble. John Wright has sent me to tell if you will give up, he would see that you would be treated with kindness." The word that I sent back was, "I have done nothing to give up for, and that if he wants to kill me, I won't agree to that."

There was a small brick house near the dwelling house. I took some bricks out of the wall making holes about eight inches square, to shoot through. I placed my guns and men in readiness for an attack. I hung lanterns to give light at night, so that they couldn't slip up and dynamite our house. We held this position for about twenty days but no one showed up.

Chapter XV

Trip to Bell County Court

"We all left our homes in Kentucky to go to court in Bell County, Kentucky, all armed with revolvers," Noah Reynolds wrote. "Both factions met at Norton, Virginia, where we were to take the train—about one hundred men and women, all mad. Once in a while some of the women would say something that sounded like it would start trouble. We all procured tickets. Train time came. We started to board the train. Joe Doody being the conductor (and a mighty fine man), and fearing there was going to be trouble, said, 'I am afraid I can't take you all on the train at this time. Mr. Reynolds, won't you wait until tomorrow?'

"I said, 'I would rather not, as I am under bond to appear in court in the morning, and I don't want to give my bondsmen any trouble. I will promise you on my part that I, nor none of my men, won't have any trouble if some one else don't start it.'

"Then John Wright stepped up and said, 'Mr. Doody, I don't think there will be any trouble. When we fight, we fight, and when we law, we law.'

"I then said, 'John Wright, you take your men in one coach and I will take mine in another.'

"Then Mr. Doody agreed to let us board the train,

129

knowing John Wright and I had bought all our tickets in clubs together. Not many passengers boarded the train that night, as the news went on ahead that the Reynolds and Wright feudites were on the train. We reached Pineville without trouble."

Martha Jane Wright, wife of Sam Wright, and sister of Noah and John Reynolds, was "kidnapped" by the commonwealth's attorney before the trial began in Pineville. Martha Jane Wright was one of the most intelligent women, and the most forthright, in the mountains. Her education was excellent for her time and place. Her mind recorded events, dates, incidents, places, and names photographically. And in this case, she had the best of reasons for recalling the incidents that heaped upon her misery almost unbearable. Two of her brothers were on one side of the Reynolds-Wright vendetta, her husband on the other, along with his brother, John Wright.

The commonwealth's attorney, learning of Martha Jane Wright's background, summoned her as a commonwealth's witness, and locked her in a room with the other state's witnesses until the trial was over. It was overwhelmingly believed that if she had been allowed to testify for the defense, her testimony would have had immense influence in favor of her brothers.

This was the same Martha Jane Wright who arranged the peace conference, which proved to be successful. The feud between John Wright and Clabe Jones and Talt Hall had ended slowly, but surely. When it was over, she had been happy and thankful. She had not been able to look forward to the day when her own life's trials would be put in the balance. But Martha Jane lived through this, to see her brothers free again, and prominent persons.

TRIAL OF NOAH REYNOLDS

At the regular term of the Bell County circuit court, Noah Reynolds was put on trial for the killing of W. S.

130

Wright. After fourteen days of court proceedings, the accused was sentenced to life imprisonment. On April 2, 1902, he was taken to the penitentiary, where his brother John Reynolds was serving fifteen years for the death of William Wright.

"I served as a trusty prisoner in a suit of honor," Noah Reynolds wrote. "I petitioned Governor Beckham for a pardon. He refused to grant it. He had already granted a pardon to Brother John some time before I put my application in. I was held in prison until Governor Augustus E. Wilson succeeded Governor Beckham. On January 1, 1909, he pardoned me from the charge of killing W. S. Wright.

"I rejoined my family, who had now moved to Knott County, Kentucky, bought them a farm on a creek known as Little Betty Troublesome, where I now live [at the time of writing his small biography], with and among a host of friends.

"John H. Reynolds [his brother], returning home from prison, went to the State of Virginia to live. Marrying Miss Carrie Addington, the daughter of Philmore Addington, he lived a quiet and peaceable life. He served as a policeman at Jenkins, for two years. Then he was appointed as prohibition agent for the eastern part of Kentucky, his headquarters being at Lexington, Kentucky. His home now was at Pikeville, Kentucky.

"On a raid in Johnson County, Kentucky, after a band of moonshiners, came in contact with a band of the McKinseys, who were moonshiners and headed by Joseph Patton McKinsey. He was killed [there] on the 26th day of August, 1921. Six of these moonshiners are serving [were serving at the time of Reynolds' publication] life terms in the penitentiary for his [John Reynolds's] murder.

"I was converted in the year 1914, and joined the Old Regular Baptist Church. The church very soon authorized me to preach. My church is one of the largest in the
131

mountains, having one hundred and forty seven members, and belongs to the Indian Bottom Association. My lot has been cast as a minister of the Gospel in the mountain parts of Kentucky. Tilden Wright, my old enemy. W. S. Wright's oldest son, joined the church the same day that I did. He joined the Thornton Church of Indian Bottom Association. Our churches are of the same faith and order, and our Associations have fellowship with each other. His church authorized him to preach. We often meet together."

Chapter XVI

John Wright Passes

John Wright had made friends with the first coal men who had come to the upper Elkhorn Valley and Kentucky River section. He had guided Captain Richard M. Broas, the eminent engineer, and his crew, into every stream and mountain fingering and crisscrossing in the area. And this finally brought him into favor with the officials of the Consolidation Coal Company, when the modern mining city of Jenkins was built in 1911-12. Wright remained a "guide" in various capacities for these leaders until his retirement. In 1916 he was elected as magistrate of the territory comprising Jenkins. He had served in this capacity in the early 1880s.

On March 12, 1925, his loyal Bluegrass wife, Martha, but called "Mattie" by her hundreds of friends, died. She was one year older than her husband. She was 82, dying on her birthday.

Martha Humphrey, a product of the level country around Lexington, had never seen the mountains until she accompanied her husband here, soon after their marriage. At once, she captured the hearts of the mountain people, especially those of the women. Soon, they nicknamed her "Mattie." When the house at Jenkins, named for her, had to go for progress, it brought sadness, not

When coal mining began in earnest, railroads laid tracks on thousands of miles of hitherto impenetrable hills during latter days of "Bad" John Wright.

only to John and Martha, but to the hundreds who had learned to love Mattie, and who, like her, felt an interest in the home.

Not long after the death of Martha, John Wright retired from active duty at Jenkins, and moved to his home at Horse Gap, near Pound, Virginia, and some seven miles from Jenkins. The old mellowed home here, sat on a rise, overlooking a branch of Pound River, and in view of the modern highway, U.S. 23.

In his eighty-seventh year, Mr. Wright was converted and joined the *old regular* Baptist Church. This religious body, before the splits with the Calvinists and the United Baptists, was by far the largest in the.mountains. This organization, following the divisions, insisted that the word

"*Old*" precede *Regular,* to distinguish definitely between it and all others. They still love this adjective.

Mr. Wright was baptized in a crystal clear hole of water near his home. Over three thousand were present in honor of this marvelous occasion. Reputedly this event drew the largest crowd ever assembled in Wise County, Virginia, exceeding even those attending the hangings of Talt Hall and Dr. Taylor at Wise.

John Wright died January 30, 1931, at the age of eighty-nine. He had seen his end coming, and had his coffin made of flawless walnut from his own farm. He was buried near his home at Horse Gap. Over three thousand people gathered!

Thus passed the last of the old warriors. Two of the notorious quartet, Talt Hall and Dr. M. B. Taylor, had died on the scaffold, but both Clabe Jones and John Wright had died and were buried with honors. There will be those who deny this statement, and that can be expected. Differing opinions have attended all such men during such years. But we wonder what would have been the fate of the law-abiding citizens, . . . the innocent, the God-fearing people, had there not been a John Wright to protect them. Although men died at the hands of the lawmen, at last in the Pine Mountain area comes peace. Once again, in the hills stilled with continued silence, we hear the musical echo of the singing of the birds, gospel songs of the righteous seemingly led by a low still voice from beyond, voices sounding in the wilderness swiftly flowing as the ripple of the water beneath the tall pines . . . a people dedicated to morality, Christianity, and Southern hospitality at last bound together with a true bond of continuous love.

The letter from Martha J. Wright reads as follows on pages 136 and 137.

Mr & Mrs S.C. _____ Hellier Ky

Dear Mr Ratliff

I will try and give some __ at last. But I
can't give all for my mother was James Born May 1870
Died aug the 8 __ 28 __ Johnie was Born aug 17th 1873
was killed Sept 12th 1898. Both were Buried at Dunham Ky
James Died with dropsy _____
that this __ died march 12th 1925 Being six year older
than this __ died on her Birth
than the this day of __ John M Wright __
__ March 14 __
give have it __ Rights about old Grandfather Wrights this
name was Gall __ it had 4 Bro's so __ Jessee Martin
John __ Wright had 4 Bro's so __ Jessee Martin
and Sam, Martin and Sam are still alive and live

136

his this community —
Sam killed at Avon, when was John elected Magistrate
at...? you have at Ky. Lt. of
I did not make the round this permanent home
I'll after mother's death 6 years ago, I hope
at Jarvil out where John and Edward...married
can get that at Pikeville, Ky. county Clerk office

you are welcome to all information I can give
you. Wat and Lol of his mistake
he said he guessed I was right. I hope you can
read this and will excuse my bad writing
I as ever Martha J. Wright

137

[Note: The above letter was a reply to the letter written by G. C. Ratliff dated March 14, 1931, almost fifty years ago as of this writing.]

The following is a letter from Ira Mullins telling about the baptism of John Wright where three thousand people were present, and also about John Wright's burial attendance of over three thousand people, letter dated May 27, 1931: